Name: ____________________

GL

Mathematics

11+ Practice Papers

David E Hanson

GL Assessment produces annual and bespoke 11+ tests for a range of schools and does not make past papers available to pupils. However, the feedback from our specialist team of 11+ tutors, independent schools' teachers, test writers and specialist authors enables us to provide you with a series of tests equipping your child with the highest level preparation. This publication covers standard question types representative of the GL range of assessments, tracking trends and levels of difficulty from the last several years. Tests can change from year to year and there is therefore no guarantee that all question types your child will encounter are represented in this publication.

Orders: **Teachers** please contact Bookpoint Ltd, 130 Park Drive, Milton Park, Abingdon, Oxon OX14 4SE. Telephone: (44) 01235 400555. Email primary@bookpoint.co.uk. Lines are open from 9 a.m. to 5 p.m., Monday to Saturday, with a 24-hour message answering service.

Parents, Tutors please call: 020 3122 6405 (Monday to Friday, 9:30 a.m. to 4.30 p.m.).
Email: parentenquiries@galorepark.co.uk
Visit our website at www.galorepark.co.uk for details of other revision guides for Common Entrance, examination papers and Galore Park publications.

ISBN: 978 1 510449 75 6

First published in 2019 by
Hodder & Stoughton Limited
An Hachette UK Company
Carmelite House
50 Victoria Embankment
London EC4Y 0DZ
www.galorepark.co.uk
Impression number 10 9 8 7 6 5 4 3 2 1
Year 2023 2022 2021 2020 2019

Illustrations by Integra Software Services Pvt. Ltd., Pondicherry, India

Typeset in India
Printed in the UK

A catalogue record for this title is available from the British Library.

Contents and progress record

Go to the Galore Park website to download the free PDF answer sheets to use and re-use as many times as you need: galorepark.co.uk/answersheets

How to use this book

Introduction

These practice papers test and encourage pupils in preparation for the GL 11+ mathematics tests, including the bespoke tests created by GL for individual schools. To give you the best chance of success, Galore Park has worked with 11+ tutors, independent schools' teachers, test writers and specialist authors to create these practice papers.

This book includes four model papers. The four papers will help to assess a pupil's knowledge, skills, understanding and reasoning ability across all areas of mathematics.

The papers are designed to:

- develop and perfect examination technique for GL 11+ tests
- give practice in answering questions in both multiple-choice and standard formats (each paper has 50 questions, worth 1 mark each)
- encourage pupils to improve their speed when taking timed papers (50 minutes should be allowed for each paper)
- help pupils identify weaker areas and improve results by studying the answers, guidance and links to revision materials.

The papers increase in difficulty from Paper 1 to Paper 4 and all work to a timing that has been typical of GL tests in the past. This is because GL tests can change in difficulty both from year to year and from school to school.

You will find that you are asked to record your answers in two different ways:

- choosing a multiple-choice option using a separate answer sheet (Papers 1 to 3)
- writing a complete answer on the paper itself (Paper 4).

You are being given practice in working with these different styles since the tests may come in either of these formats or as an online test. The styles used in the multiple-choice tests are similar to the question styles you will find in the online tests.

As you mark your answers, you will see references to the Galore Park *11+ Mathematics Revision Guide*. These references have been included so that you can go straight to some useful revision tips and find extra practice questions for those areas where you would like more help.

Working through the book

The **Contents and progress record** on page 3 helps you to track your scores and timings as you work through the papers.

You may find some of the questions hard, but don't worry – these tests are designed to make you think. Agree with your parents on a good time to take the test and follow the instructions below to prepare for each paper as if you are actually going to sit your Pre-test/11+ mathematics test.

1. Check at the beginning of the paper if you will be recording your answers on an **answer sheet**. If a sheet is required, download it from www.galorepark.co.uk/answersheets and print it out before you begin.
2. Take the test in a quiet room. Set a timer and record your answers as instructed.
3. Note down how long the paper takes you (questions should take an average of about 1 minute each to answer; all questions should be completed even if you run over the time suggested). Aim to complete the paper in the time you are advised. If possible, complete a whole paper in one session.
4. Mark the paper using the answers at the back of the book.
5. Go through the paper again with a friend or parent, talk about the difficult questions and note which parts of the revision guide you are going to review.

The **Answers** can be cut out so that you can mark your papers easily. Do not look at the answers until you have attempted a whole paper.

When you have finished a complete paper, turn back to the **Contents and progress record** and fill in the **Score** and **Time** boxes.

If you would like to take further GL-style papers after completing this book, you will find more papers in the *Pre-test/11+ Mathematics Practice Papers 1 and 2* (see Continue your learning journey on page 7).

Test day tips

Take time to prepare yourself on the day before you go for the test. Remember to take sharpened pencils, an eraser and, if you are allowed, water to maintain your concentration levels and a watch to time yourself.

... and don't forget to have breakfast before you go!

Pre-test and the 11+ entrance exams

This title is part of the Galore Park *Pre-test/11+* series and there are four further *Mathematics Practice Paper* titles (see **Continue your learning journey** on page 7).

This series is designed to help you prepare for Pre-tests and 11+ entrance exams if you are applying to independent schools. These exams are often the same as those set by local grammar schools.

Pre-tests and 11+ mathematics tests appear in a variety of formats and lengths and it is likely that if you are applying for more than one school, you will encounter more than one of style of test. These include:

- Pre-test/11+ entrance exams in different formats from GL, CEM and ISEB
- Pre-test/11+ entrance exams created specifically for particular schools.

As the tests change all the time it can be difficult to predict the questions, making them harder to revise for. If you are taking more than one style of test, review the books in the **Continue your learning journey** section to see which other titles could be helpful to you.

For parents

For your child to get the maximum benefit from these papers, they should complete them in conditions as close as possible to those they will face in the actual test, as described in the **Working through the book** section on page 5.

Working with your child to follow up the revision work suggested in the answers can improve their performance in areas where they are less confident and boost their chances of success.

For teachers and tutors

The timing of all papers is the same in this *Practice Papers* book since fast timing isn't generally a feature of GL-style papers.

The answer sheets provide helpful practice in recording answers on a separate document. The standard-format test includes questions that require lateral thinking, typical of the most challenging assessments.

Remediation suggested in the answers, referencing the *Revision Guide*, can be helpful for follow-up revision having completed the paper.

Continue your learning journey

When you have completed these *Practice Papers*, you can carry on your learning right up until exam day with the following resources.

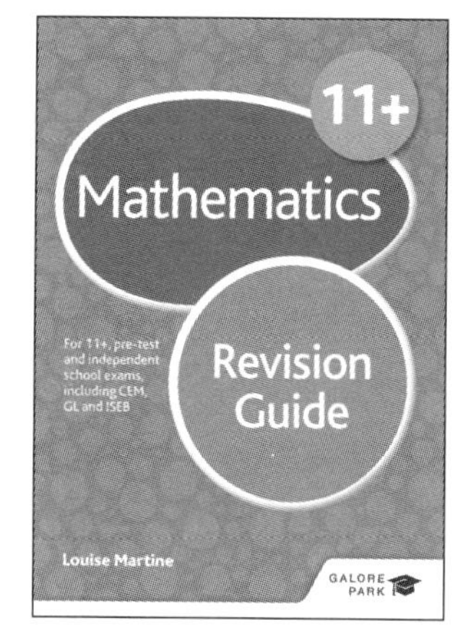

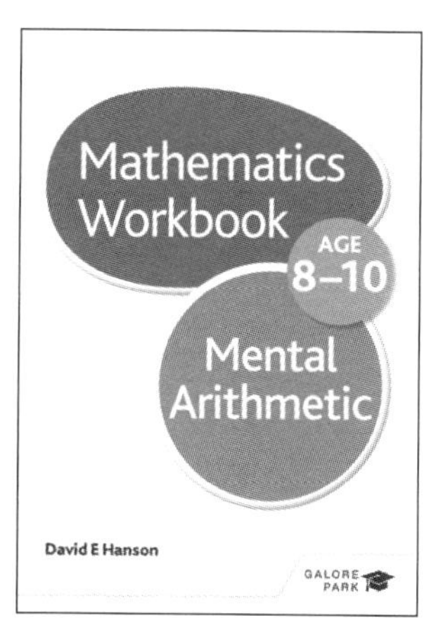

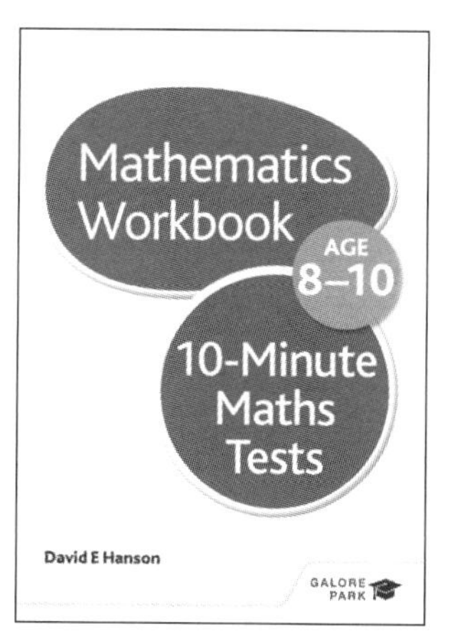

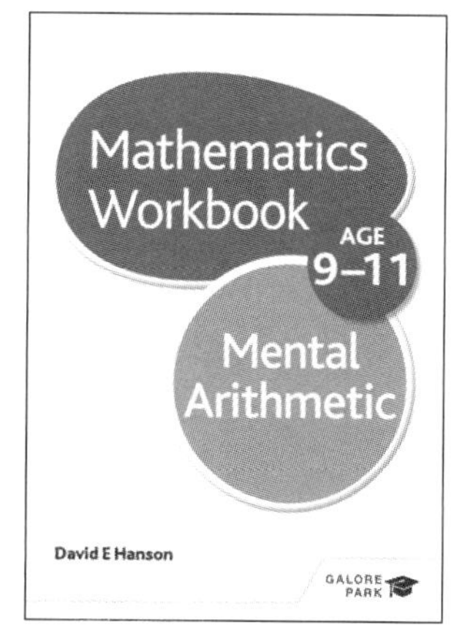

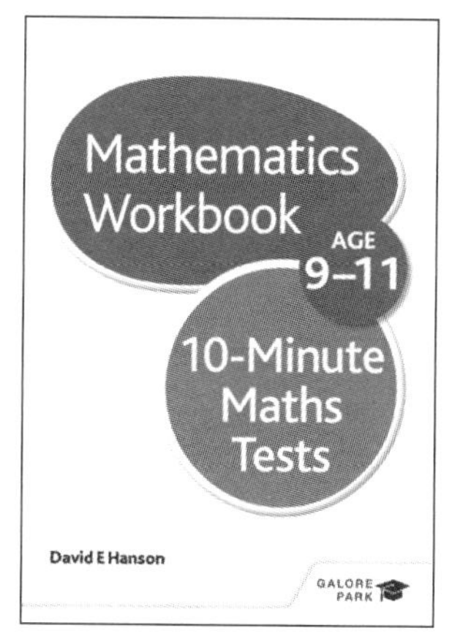

The *Revision Guide* (referenced in the answers to this book) reviews basic skills in all areas of mathematics, and guidance is provided on how to improve in this subject.

Pre-test/11+ Practice Papers 1 and *2* are designed to provide a complete revision experience across the various test styles you may encounter. Between the two titles there are 13 model papers.

- *Book 1* begins with training tests, and contains a further series of test papers designed to develop your confidence and speed.
- *Book 2* contains GL-style tests and bespoke papers intended for pupils taking the most advanced tests delivered at independent schools.

CEM 11+ Mathematics Practice Papers test and encourage you in preparation for the mathematics content of CEM 11+ tests, including the bespoke tests created by CEM for individual schools. The four papers will help to assess your knowledge, skills, understanding and reasoning ability across all areas of mathematics.

The two *Workbooks* (*Mental Arithmetic* and *10-Minute Maths Tests*) will further develop your skills with 50 mental arithmetic tests and 80 10-minute tests to work through. These titles include more examples of the different types of questions you meet in these *Practice Papers* – the more times you practise the questions, the better equipped for the exams you will be.

Use Atom Learning to improve familiarity with online tests: the online learning platform adapts to your ability to ensure you are always working on your optimal learning path and the adaptive, mock-testing facility looks and scores in the style of the pre-tests.

galorepark.co.uk/atomlearning

Paper 1

Test time: 50 minutes

Download and print the answer sheet from galorepark.co.uk/answersheets before you start this paper.

Training question

How many two-digit multiples of 8 are there? Draw a clear rule through the box next to your selected answer in pencil.

9	10	11	12	13
A ☐	B ☐	C ☐	D ☐	E ☐

The correct answer is at the bottom of this page.

1 How many of these letters in the word MATHS have *one and only one* line of symmetry? (1)

MATHS

1	2	3	4	5
A	B	C	D	E

2 Jane bought five pencils. She handed over a £2 coin and received 95p change.
What was the cost of one pencil? (1)

24p	21p	22p	23p	25p
A	B	C	D	E

3 Which group of numbers contains only prime numbers? (1)

3, 7, 39	2, 11, 27	7, 13, 69	2, 23, 37	5, 11, 21
A	B	C	D	E

4 The diagram below shows the results when the pupils in a school were asked if they owned a cycle.

	boys	girls
own a cycle	47	37
do not own a cycle	23	28

How many more pupils own a cycle than do not own a cycle? (1)

43	13	33	24	10
A	B	C	D	E

5 Sam thought of a number, multiplied it by 4 and then subtracted 5
The result was 23
What number did Sam think of? (1)

6	7	8	$6\frac{1}{2}$	$7\frac{1}{2}$
A	B	C	D	E

The answer is C 11
The multiples are: 16 (two 8s), 24, 32, 40, 48, 56, 64, 72, 80, 88, 96 (twelve 8s)

6 What is the product of 39 and 47? (1)

1836	1683	1833	1823	1933
A	B	C	D	E

7 Caden scored the following numbers of goals in four football matches:

3 6 0 1

What is Caden's median score? (1)

2	3	$3\frac{1}{2}$	4	5
A	B	C	D	E

8 What is the area of the rectangle? (1)

3.5 cm

5 cm

15.5 cm²	16.5 cm²	17.25 cm²	17.5 cm²	18.5 cm²
A	B	C	D	E

9 Which of the following numbers has the largest number of factors, including itself and 1? (1)

10	12	16	19	22
A	B	C	D	E

10 Kaylee went shopping with a £20 note. She bought two DVDs costing £5.95 each. She wrote down the total cost and the change she would get from the £20 note.

Which two amounts did Kaylee write down? (1)

£11.90 £9.10	£11.90 £8.10	£10.90 £8.10	£12.90 £8.10	£10.90 £9.10
A	B	C	D	E

11 It is known that $18.5 \times 3.8 = 70.3$

Using this fact, what is the value of $140.6 \div 18.5$? (1)

1.9	7.4	3.8	7.6	1.8
A	B	C	D	E

12 The two-stage function machine below multiplies an input by 3 and then subtracts 4

Input **?** → × 3 → − 4 → Output **20**

If the machine output is 20, what was the input? (1)

16	6	7	8	$5\frac{1}{3}$
A	B	C	D	E

13 Sally has eleven coins.

She has four £1 coins and the rest are 20p coins.

What is the total value of Sally's coins? (1)

£5.60	£6.40	£6.20	£5.20	£5.40
A	B	C	D	E

14 Estimate how many 10p coins could be placed, in a single layer, to cover this page. (1)

50	100	150	200	250
A	B	C	D	E

15 How many of the numbers below are divisible by 7? (1)

14 56 91 72 28 63

2	3	4	5	6
A	B	C	D	E

16 Louise has a favourite number. When she doubles her number and then subtracts 4, the result is a number that is 2 more than her favourite number.

What is Louise's favourite number? (1)

4	5	6	7	8
A	B	C	D	E

17 The pictogram below shows the number of pets seen by a vet during one week.

dogs	
cats	

One symbol represents **two** pets.

How many more dogs than cats did he see? (1)

3	5	6	7	9
A	B	C	D	E

18 In London, the temperature is 14 °C.

In Aviemore, the temperature is 18 degrees lower than in London.

In Edinburgh, it is 5 degrees warmer than it is in Aviemore.

What is the temperature in Edinburgh? (1)

−2 °C	−1 °C	0 °C	1 °C	2 °C
A	B	C	D	E

19 The three number cards below can be placed side by side to make three-digit numbers. For example:

3 4 5 → 345

How many different three-digit numbers, including 345, can be made using these cards? (1)

3	4	5	6	7
A	B	C	D	E

20 What is a quarter of 62? (1)

14	$14\frac{1}{2}$	15	$15\frac{1}{4}$	$15\frac{1}{2}$
A	B	C	D	E

21 The two-digit number 43 has a digit sum of 7 because $4 + 3 = 7$
How many two-digit numbers between 10 and 100 have a digit sum of 5? (1)

3	4	5	6	7
A	B	C	D	E

22 At Grange School, 123 children walk to school, 39 are taken by car and 18 are taken in a minibus.
How many children are at Grange School? (1)

170	175	180	185	190
A	B	C	D	E

23 The total cost of the items in Ms Brown's shopping was £53.19 but, because of special offers, the total she had to pay was reduced by £4.25
How much did Ms Brown pay for her shopping? (1)

£57.44	£48.84	£49.84	£48.94	£48.44
A	B	C	D	E

24 Mirjana bought some chocolate bars costing 42 pence each.
She received £2.48 in change from a £5 note.
How many chocolate bars did Mirjana buy? (1)

5	6	7	8	9
A	B	C	D	E

25 What are the co-ordinates of the point *P*? (1)

1
0 1 2
P

(1.3, 1.1)	(1.1, 1.3)	(1.2, 1.6)	(1.6, 1.1)	(1.6, 1.2)
A	B	C	D	E

26 The diagram below shows a maze.

Isaac writes down his route. For example, N3 represents north 3 squares.

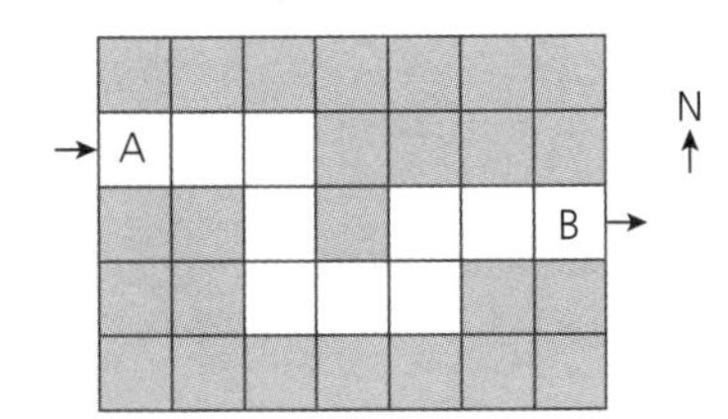

Which of the following shows Isaac's route from square A to square B? **(1)**

- A W2-S2-E2-N1-E2
- B E2-S2-E2-N1-W2
- C W2-S2-E2-N1-E2
- D E2-S2-W2-N1-E2
- E E2-S2-E2-N1-E2

27 12 apples cost £3.60

What is the cost of 18 apples? **(1)**

£5.40	£4.80	£5.00	£5.60	£5.20
A	B	C	D	E

28 Which number is closest to 3? **(1)**

3.1	2.9	2.95	3.04	2.94
A	B	C	D	E

29 Zara's height is 5 ft.

Which is closest to her height in centimetres? **(1)**

140 cm	145 cm	150 cm	155 cm	160 cm
A	B	C	D	E

30 In four years' time, May will be twice as old as she was two years ago.

How old is May now? **(1)**

4	6	7	8	9
A	B	C	D	E

31 What is the value of $2 \times 4 + 7 - 5 \times 3$? **(1)**

−2	0	2	7	36
A	B	C	D	E

32 What is the perimeter of the shape? **(1)**

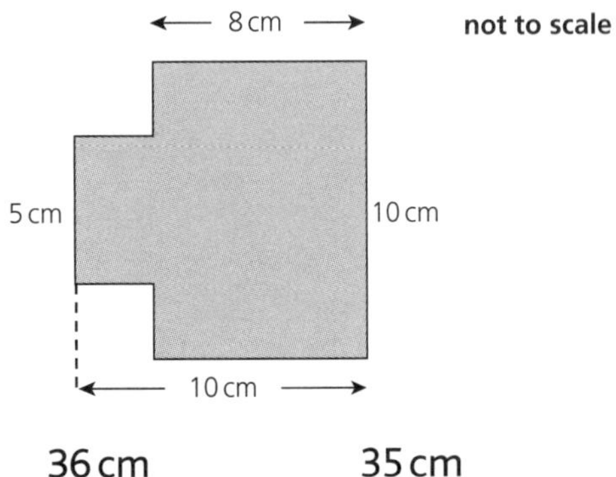

36 cm	35 cm	42 cm	40 cm	100 cm
A	B	C	D	E

33 To calculate the number of sausage rolls, n, needed for a party, Mrs James uses the formula:

$n = 2a + 3c + 5$

where a is the number of adults and c is the number of children.

How many sausage rolls should she make for a party where there will be 4 adults and 6 children? (1)

10	15	26	31	65
A	B	C	D	E

34 The diagram shows part of a jumbled multiplication square.

×	6	8	9	7
6	36	48	54	42
9	54	72		63
7	42		63	49
8	48	64	72	56

Which two numbers are missing? (1)

81, 63	48, 63	81, 64	54, 72	56, 81
A	B	C	D	E

35 When the following decimals are arranged in order of increasing size, which one will be in the middle? (1)

3.023 3.203 2.303 2.33 3.22

3.023	3.203	2.303	2.33	3.22
A	B	C	D	E

36 Eva has saved £140 towards a new bicycle that costs £400

What percentage of the cost has Eva saved? (1)

15%	20%	25%	30%	35%
A	B	C	D	E

37 What fraction, in its lowest terms (simplest form), of the regular hexagon is shaded? (1)

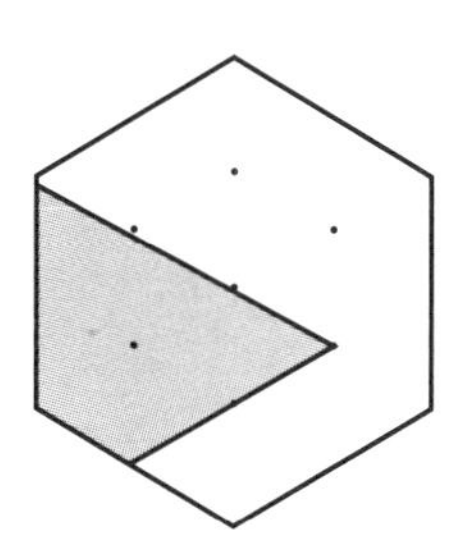

$\frac{1}{3}$	$\frac{4}{11}$	$\frac{5}{12}$	$\frac{6}{15}$	$\frac{3}{7}$
A	B	C	D	E

38 Tammy has the coloured counters shown in her pocket.

Tammy picks a counter at random from her pocket.
What is the probability that Tammy will pick a white counter? (1)

$\frac{1}{8}$	$\frac{1}{4}$	$\frac{3}{7}$	$\frac{3}{8}$	$\frac{1}{2}$
A	B	C	D	E

39 Brian's calculator showed the display below.

3.44532

What is this number written to two decimal places? (1)

3.4	3.44	3.445	3.45	3.445
A	B	C	D	E

40 What is the approximate value (to the nearest 100) of the product 48×52? (1)

2000	2300	2400	2500	2600
A	B	C	D	E

41 Charlie leaves home at 08:37 and arrives at school at 09:13
How long does it take Charlie to walk to school? (1)

30 minutes	33 minutes	34 minutes	36 minutes	43 minutes
A	B	C	D	E

42 Bella shares her birthday cake with three friends.
Amy and Bella have two slices each, Chloe has three slices and Donna has one slice.
There are four slices left.
What fraction of the whole cake has Bella eaten? (1)

$\frac{1}{8}$	$\frac{1}{6}$	$\frac{1}{5}$	$\frac{1}{4}$	$\frac{1}{3}$
A	B	C	D	E

43 What is the number 45.445 rounded to three significant figures? (1)

45	45.4	45.44	45.5	45.45
A	B	C	D	E

44 How many small triangles will there be in the next pattern in this sequence? (1)

14	15	16	17	18
A	B	C	D	E

45 Two angles of a triangle are 54° and 72°.
Which of the following words accurately describes the triangle? (1)

right-angled	equilateral	obtuse-angled	isosceles	scalene
A	B	C	D	E

46 What is 18% of £400? (1)

£50	£54	£64	£72	£80
A	B	C	D	E

47 How many of the shapes below have rotational symmetry of order 2? (1)

2	3	4	5	6
A	B	C	D	E

48 A circle has radius 12 cm.
What is the approximate circumference of the circle? (1)

6 cm	24 cm	36 cm	72 cm	432 cm
A	B	C	D	E

49 What is the sum of 12.49 and 89.08? (1)

92.57	101.57	102.29	102.57	102.67
A	B	C	D	E

50 Bill and Ben share a bag of 45 sweets in the ratio 5:4
How many more sweets does Bill eat than Ben eats? (1)

1	3	4	5	9
A	B	C	D	E

Paper 2

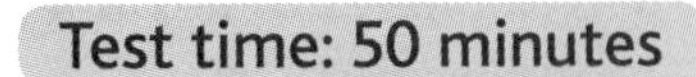

Test time: 50 minutes

Download and print the answer sheet from galorepark.co.uk/answersheets before you start this paper.

1 Year 6 carried out a survey into favourite ice cream flavours and represented their results in a bar chart.

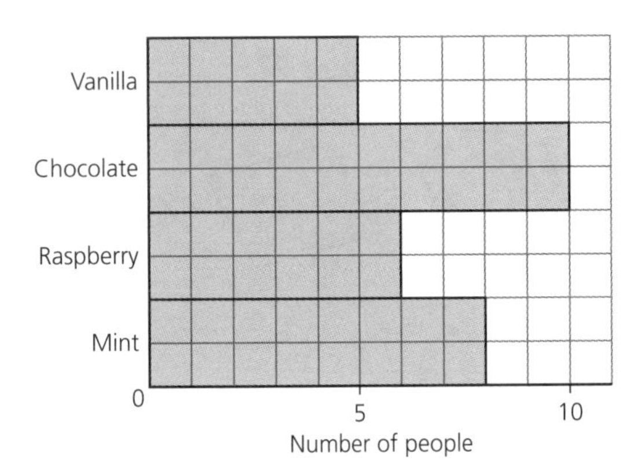

How many pupils took part in the survey? (1)

4	26	27	28	29
A	B	C	D	E

2 In a group of 24 people, five-sixths are aged 16 years or older.
How many are aged under 16? (1)

2	4	6	8	18
A	B	C	D	E

3 James has 60 identical balls with a total mass of 1 kg 50 g.
He divides the balls into three equal groups.
What is the total mass of the balls in one group? (1)

50 g	300 g	350 g	500 g	750 g
A	B	C	D	E

4 Which letter below has rotational symmetry but *not* line symmetry? (1)

B	H	O	S	X
A	B	C	D	E

5 A rectangle is twice as long as it is wide, and the perimeter is 24 cm.
How long is the rectangle? (1)

4 cm	5 cm	6 cm	7 cm	8 cm
A	B	C	D	E

6 In which number below does the 5 have the greatest value? (1)

5.04	3570	0.05	7050	990.5
A	B	C	D	E

7 The table shows the number of goals scored by the soccer team last season.

number of goals	0	1	2	3
number of matches	2	4	3	1

The team scored 2 goals in 3 of their matches.

How many goals did the team score altogether last season? (1)

4	8	10	13	15
A	B	C	D	E

8 Makayla bought two trays of pansies, each holding 12 plants. The total cost was £4.80
What was the cost of each pansy? (1)

10p	12p	20p	24p	40p
A	B	C	D	E

9 In a sports club, two-thirds of the members are female. There are nine males in the club.
How many members are there in the club? (1)

12	18	24	27	36
A	B	C	D	E

10 The grid contains the numbers 1 to 9

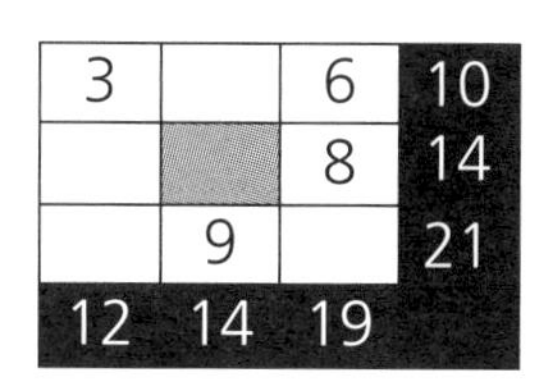

The row and column totals are printed in white on black.
What number goes in the grey box? (1)

1	2	4	5	7
A	B	C	D	E

11 Mr and Mrs Patel and their children are going to the theatre in London.
The cost of each adult ticket is £45 and the cost of each child ticket is £20
If the total cost of the tickets is £210, how many children are there in the Patel family? (1)

2	3	4	5	6
A	B	C	D	E

12 On the grid below, three of the corners of a square are marked with crosses.

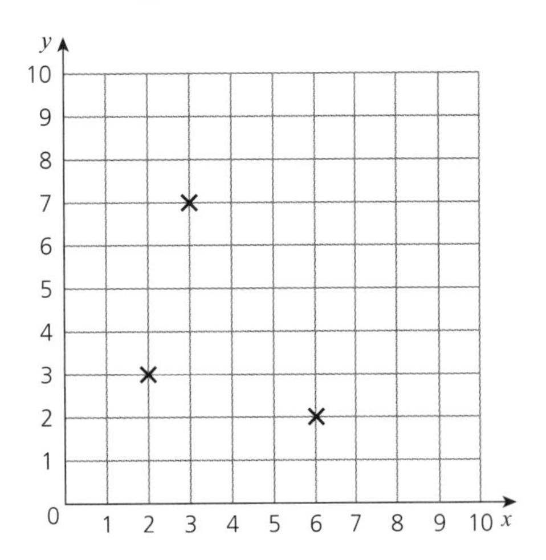

What are the co-ordinates of the fourth corner of the square? **(1)**

(6, 7)	(7, 6)	(8, 8)	(7, 7)	(8, 7)
A	B	C	D	E

13 200 millilitres of lemonade from a new two-litre bottle is poured into each of seven glasses.

What volume of lemonade will be left in the bottle? **(1)**

200 ml	0.3 litres	350 ml	400 ml	0.6 litres
A	B	C	D	E

14 Barry has eaten two-fifths of his birthday cake.

He says Mhairi can eat a third of what is left.

What fraction of the whole cake will Mhairi eat? **(1)**

a tenth	a fifth	a quarter	a third	two-fifths
A	B	C	D	E

15 Which of the following numbers is divisible by both 6 and 8? **(1)**

12	16	18	24	36
A	B	C	D	E

16 A book has 40 pages and three-eighths of the pages have illustrations.

How many pages do *not* have illustrations? **(1)**

5	8	15	20	25
A	B	C	D	E

17 The machine subtracts 5 and then divides by 4

Input **23** → | $-\,5$ | $\div\,4$ | → Output **?**

When the input is 23, what is the output? **(1)**

4	$4\frac{1}{2}$	$5\frac{1}{2}$	6	7
A	B	C	D	E

18 What is the number 10.7458 written to two decimal places? (1)

10.7	10.74	10.745	10.746	10.75
A	B	C	D	E

19 Which of the following shapes has the largest number of lines of symmetry? (1)

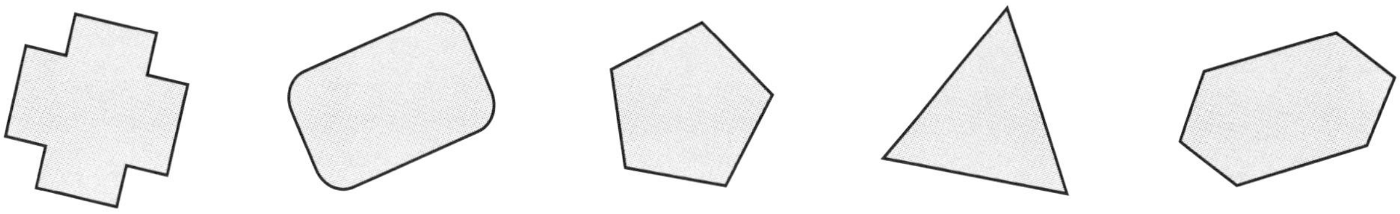

A	B	C	D	E

20 Jamie has three turns on each ride at the theme park.

sky train	£4.50
big splash	£4.00
wonder wheel	£3.50

What is the total cost? (1)

£30.00	£36.00	£24.00	£32.50	£12.00
A	B	C	D	E

21 Samantha's dog Rosie was y years old when Samantha was born.

Rosie is now 13 years old.

How old is Samantha? (1)

$\frac{y}{13}$	$y - 13$	y	$y + 13$	$13 - y$
A	B	C	D	E

22 For the school outing, two buses, each capable of seating 52 people, transport the adults and children.

There is one adult for every 6 children.

If there are 6 empty seats, how many children are on the outing? (1)

84	98	42	64	72
A	B	C	D	E

23 Amy has baked a tray of muffins.

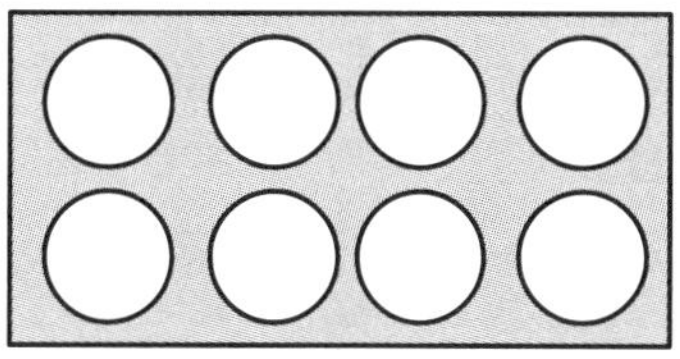

Amy eats two of the muffins.

What percentage of the muffins is left? (1)

6%	25%	75%	60%	80%
A	B	C	D	E

24 A model aeroplane, normally priced at £10.50, is reduced by 20% in the sale.
What is the sale price? (1)

£2.10	£8.40	£6.05	£8.50	£12.60
A	B	C	D	E

25 The picture shows a bag of vegetables on a balance.

The needle shows the mass in kilograms.

What would be the reading on the balance if 500 g of vegetables were removed from the sack? (1)

0.9 kg	1.9 kg	1.7 kg	0.8 kg	2.2 kg
A	B	C	D	E

26 Here is the piece of a puzzle with area 9 cm².

3 cm

3 cm

What is the perimeter of the piece? (1)

15 cm	18 cm	12 cm	14 cm	16 cm
A	B	C	D	E

27 Which of the following numbers is divisible exactly by both 6 and 7? (1)

36	54	72	84	102
A	B	C	D	E

28 Alyssa multiplied her favourite number by 4, then subtracted 6 and finally divided by 2
The result was 15
What is Alyssa's favourite number? (1)

11	10	9	8	7
A	B	C	D	E

29 The table shows the total numbers of texts sent by Chris in one week.

day	Su	M	Tu	W	Th	F	Sa
number of texts	14	22	17	31	17	40	20

What was the median number of texts sent by Chris? (1)

20	23	26	22	17
A	B	C	D	E

30 Gita has a set of 24 gardening books, each one with a thickness of 25 mm.
She puts the books side by side on a shelf measuring 1 metre exactly.
How much space is there on the shelf? (1)

20 cm	40 cm	48 cm	60 cm	80 cm
A	B	C	D	E

31 Apples cost *a* pence each and bananas cost *b* pence each.
What is the cost of 6 apples and 5 bananas? (1)

$6a + 5b$	$11ab$	$11(a + b)$	$30ab$	$a + b$
A	B	C	D	E

32 Joseph has a bag containing 20 marbles of the same size. Four marbles are blue, seven are red and the rest are green.
Joseph picks a marble at random from the bag.
Which one of the following is *not* true? (1)

A He is more likely to pick a green marble than a red marble.
B He has a more than even chance of picking a green marble.
C He is at least twice as likely to pick a green marble as a blue marble.
D He has a one in five chance of picking a blue marble.
E He is most likely to pick a marble that is not green.

33 2^4 is the same as: (1)

6	8	16	24	32
A	B	C	D	E

34 Which answer describes the four angles below, in order, from left to right? (1)

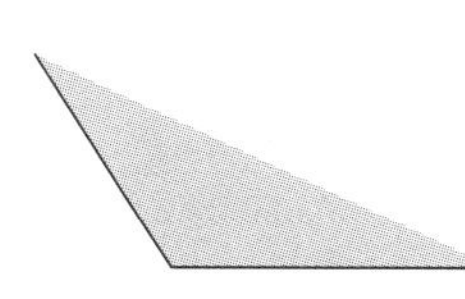
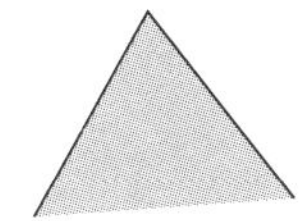
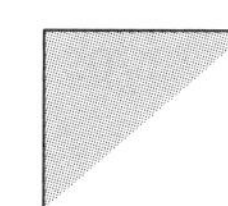

A	right angle	obtuse angle	acute angle	reflex angle
B	obtuse angle	reflex angle	right angle	acute angle
C	obtuse angle	acute angle	reflex angle	right angle
D	obtuse angle	acute angle	right angle	reflex angle
E	acute angle	obtuse angle	reflex angle	right angle

35 What is the value of $a + 2b + 3c$ when $a = 3, b = 4$ and $c = 5$? (1)

26	28	62	6	19
A	B	C	D	E

36 What is the area of the parallelogram? **(1)**

8.5 cm

7 cm

8 cm

56 cm²	59.5 cm²	68 cm²	33 cm²	30 cm²
A	B	C	D	E

37 The distance between Angleford and Bangly is 5 miles (8 kilometres).
The distance between Bangly and Dangle is 40 kilometres.
What is this distance in miles? **(1)**

8 miles	25 miles	64 miles	13 miles	22 miles
A	B	C	D	E

38 In Year 6, there are 60 children.
70% of the children in Year 6 have a dog.
How many children do *not* have a dog? **(1)**

42	70	18	56	28
A	B	C	D	E

39 Which of these routes will *not* take you from A to B? **(1)**

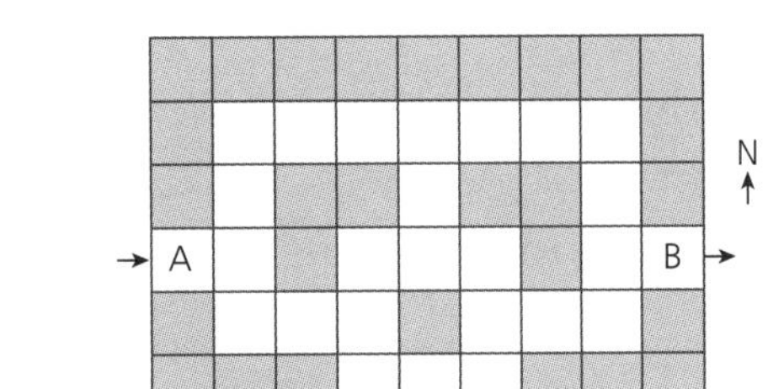

A E1-N2-E6-S2-E1
B E1-S1-E2-S1-E2-N1-E2-N1-E1
C E1-S1-E2-N1-E1-N2-E3-S2-E1
D E1-N2-E3-S2-W1-S2-E2-N1-E2-N1-E1
E E1-S1-E2-N1-E1-N2-W3-S2-W1

40 Which of the following calculations gives the largest answer? **(1)**

A $(2+3)\times5-4=$
B $2+(3\times5)-4=$
C $2+3\times5-4=$
D $2+3\times(5-4)=$
E $(2+3)\times(5-4)=$

41 Caleb has a model car made to a scale of 1:50
If the length of the real car is 4 m, what is the length of Caleb's model car? **(1)**

0.2 m	2 cm	12.5 cm	8 cm	1.25 cm
A	B	C	D	E

42 The bar chart shows the money raised by the children in a class.

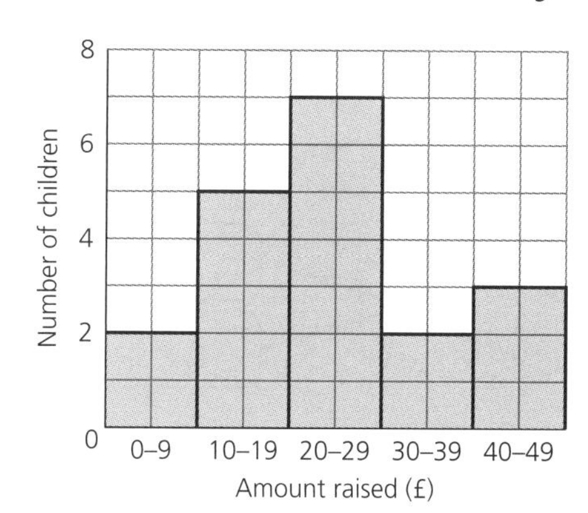

Which of the following describes the proportion of the children who raised £30 or more? (1)

half the class	$\frac{1}{3}$ of the class	more than 25%	more than half	$\frac{14}{19}$
A	B	C	D	E

43 What is half of a third of a quarter? (1)

$\frac{1}{12}$	$\frac{1}{3}$	$\frac{1}{6}$	$\frac{1}{24}$	$\frac{1}{9}$
A	B	C	D	E

44 In a right-angled triangle, one of the acute angles is twice the size of the other. What size is the smallest angle of the triangle? (1)

20°	30°	40°	45°	60°
A	B	C	D	E

45 The diagram shows a rug of area $2\,m^2$ with a pattern of squares.

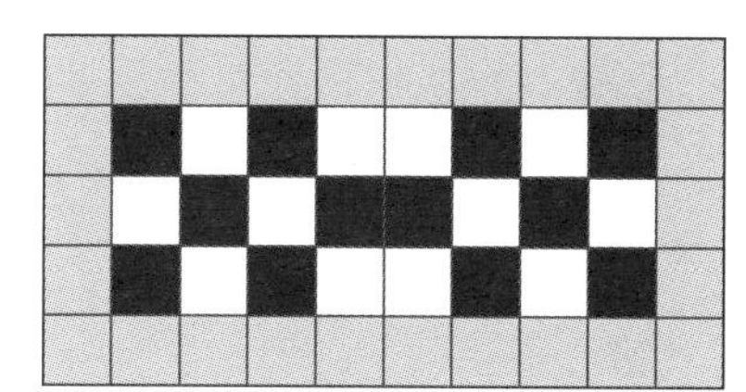

What is the total area of the black squares? (1)

$0.24\,m^2$	$0.36\,m^2$	$0.40\,m^2$	$0.48\,m^2$	$0.60\,m^2$
A	B	C	D	E

46 Which of the following refers to the faces (F), vertices (V) and edges (E) of a square-based pyramid? (1)

5 F, 5 V, 8 E	4 F, 5 V, 8 E	6 F, 6 V, 6 E	8 F, 5 V, 6 E	5 F, 4 V, 8 E
A	B	C	D	E

47 The diagram is used to sort shapes.

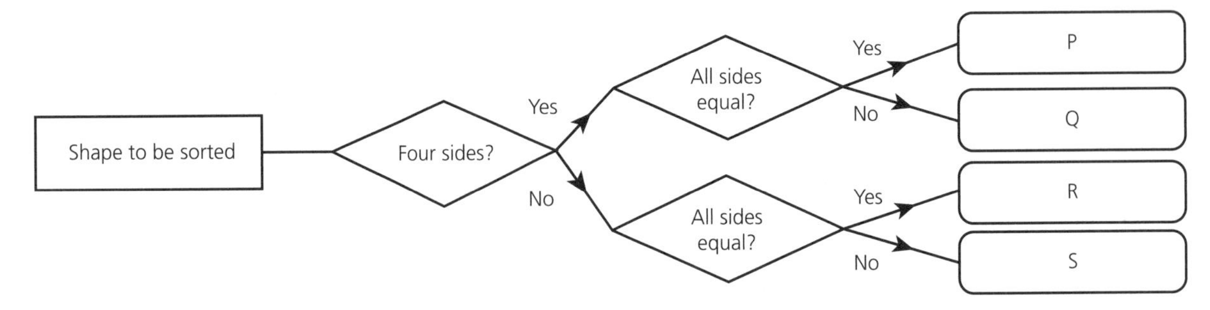

Which of the following pairs of shapes would be sorted into box Q? **(1)**

rhombus kite	square rhombus	scalene triangle parallelogram	rectangle trapezium	kite square
A	B	C	D	E

48 Which of the following does *not* give the answer 24? **(1)**

$96 \div 4$	$1\frac{1}{2} \times 16$	$\frac{2}{3}$ of 36	60% of 40	$6^2 - 2^3$
A	B	C	D	E

49 Ian has a 4 m piece of string. He keeps folding it in two until the folded string measures 25 cm.

How many times has he folded the string? **(1)**

4	5	6	7	8
A	B	C	D	E

50 In a card game, a cat scores the same as three dogs and a dog scores 3 less than a cow.

The four cards in Crystal's hand score a total of 15 points.

Which of the following groups of four cards could Crystal have? **(1)**

A cat, cat, dog, dog
B dog, dog, dog, dog
C cat, dog, dog, cow
D cat, dog, cow, cow
E cat, cat, cat, cow

Paper 3

Test time: 50 minutes

Download and print the answer sheet from galorepark.co.uk/answersheets before you start this paper.

1 Which of the following words has both vertical and horizontal line symmetry? (1)

ANNA	SOS	ELLE	OHO	OTTO
A	B	C	D	E

2 The pupils in a class were asked to choose a favourite 'supper' from the chip shop menu.

	fish	chicken	haggis
boys	5	3	4
girls	6	5	?

If there are six more girls in the class than there are boys, how many girls chose haggis? (1)

5	6	7	8	9
A	B	C	D	E

3 A large packet of breakfast flakes holds 750 grams of flakes and costs £2.40

A small packet of the same flakes holds 500 grams of flakes and costs £1.60

The Jones family eat 30 kilograms of breakfast flakes in a year.

How much money would they save (if any) in a year, by buying the flakes in large packets rather than small packets? (1)

£0	£2	£5	£10	£20
A	B	C	D	E

4 Which two numbers are missing from this table? (1)

	24	12
24		6
12	6	3

9 and 36	12 and 48	12 and 36	9 and 48	8 and 48
A	B	C	D	E

5 A farmer has a map of his field. The length of the field on the map is 10 cm and the length of the real field is 200 metres.

What is the scale of the map? (1)

1:20000	1:2000	1:200	1:20	1:10
A	B	C	D	E

6 The bar chart shows the heights of bean plants.

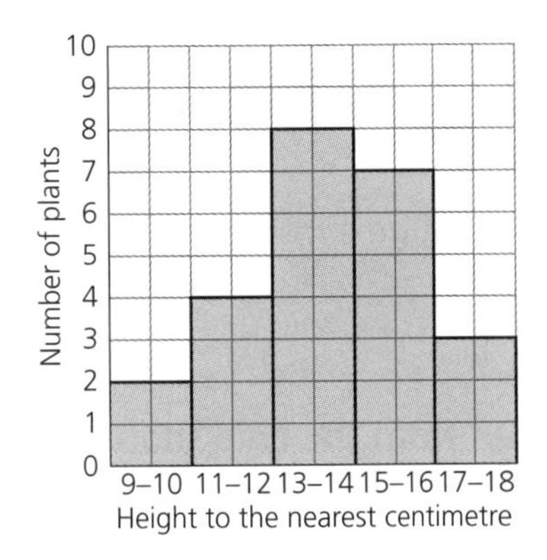

Which statement *must* be true? (1)

A Four plants are at least 17 cm tall.
B One plant is 18 cm tall.
C Most of the plants are either 13 or 14 cm tall.
D There are 25 plants in the study.
E A third of the plants are either 13 or 14 cm tall.

7 What is the time 8.45 p.m. written in the 24-hour clock? (1)

08:45	22:45	19:45	20:45	18:45
A	B	C	D	E

8 What is the approximate size of angle *a* in the parallelogram? (1)

60°	80°	100°	120°	140°
A	B	C	D	E

9 Which of these is *not* a prime number? (1)

23	43	53	63	73
A	B	C	D	E

10 What fraction of 2 kilograms is 200 grams? (1)

$\frac{1}{100}$	$\frac{1}{1000}$	$\frac{1}{10}$	$\frac{1}{20}$	$\frac{1}{4}$
A	B	C	D	E

11 What is the number 'three hundred and five thousand, three hundred and five' written in figures? (1)

350 305	305 350	305 305	350 350	3005 305
A	B	C	D	E

12 May has a favourite number. When she doubles it and then subtracts seven, she gets a number that is six more than her favourite number.

What is May's favourite number? (1)

7	11	13	17	23
A	B	C	D	E

13 The end points of five lines are given below the graph.
Which line is perpendicular to the line AB? (1)

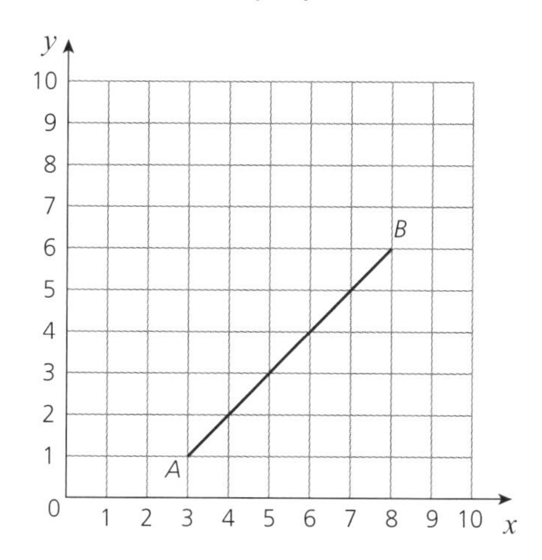

A GH G (6, 0), H (10, 4)
B IJ I (7, 2), J (3, 6)
C KL K (5, 3), L (3, 6)
D MN M (0, 10), N (8, 0)
E OP O (6, 8), P (2, 4)

14 What number does the arrow indicate on the scale? (1)

2.9	2.85	2.815	2.83	2.825
A	B	C	D	E

15 In a modern dance group there are 39 boys and 26 girls.
What fraction of the club is boys? (1)

$\frac{3}{4}$	$\frac{2}{5}$	$\frac{2}{3}$	$\frac{4}{5}$	$\frac{3}{5}$
A	B	C	D	E

16 How many of the shapes below are the same shape and size as P? (1)

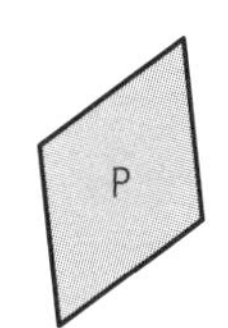

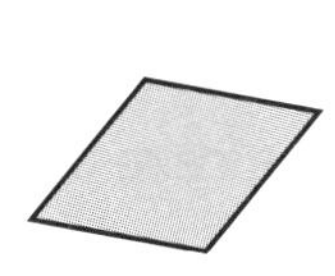
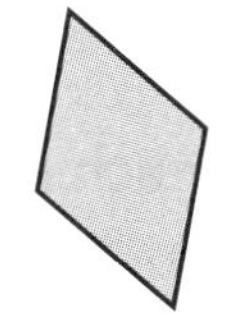
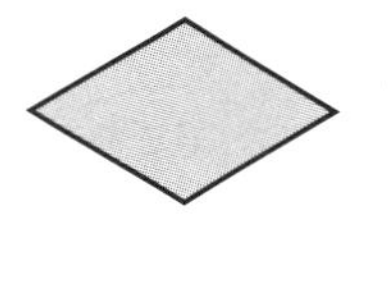
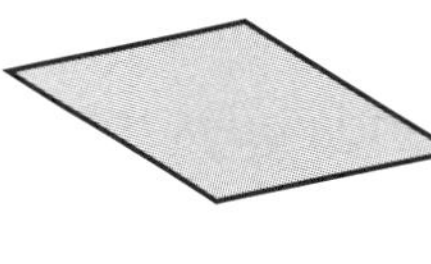

1	2	3	4	5
A	B	C	D	E

17 Which triangle is isosceles? (1)

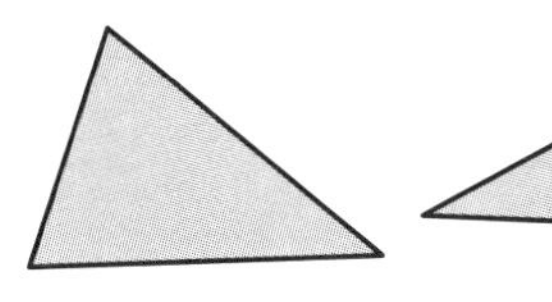
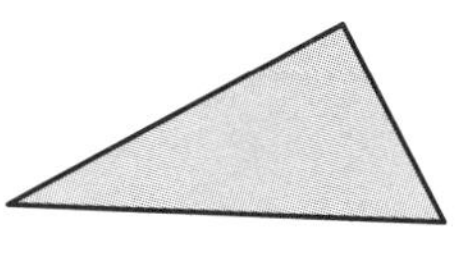
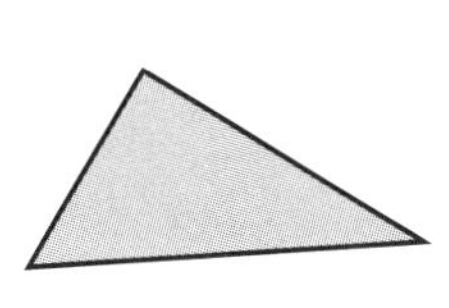
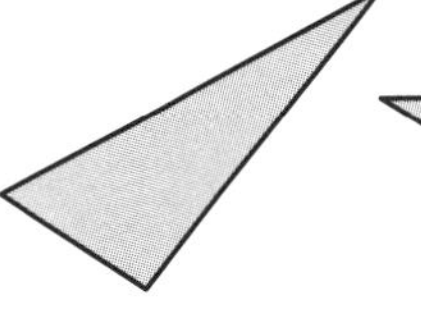
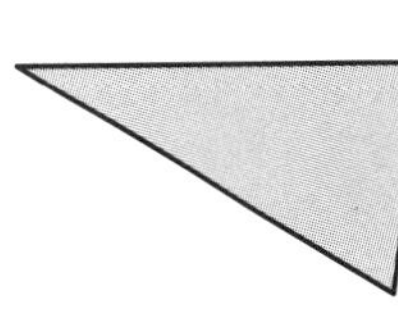

A B C D E

18 What are the co-ordinates of the cross? (1)

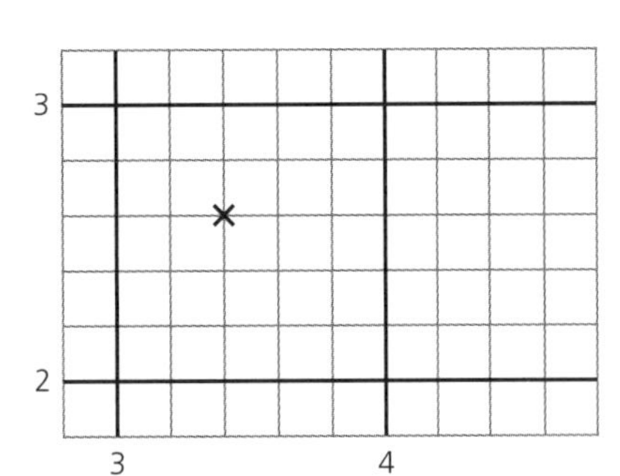

(3.4, 2.6)	(2.6, 3.4)	(3.4, 3.6)	(2.5, 2.5)	(3.6, 2.4)
A	B	C	D	E

19 In the isosceles trapezium below, angle a is 130°.

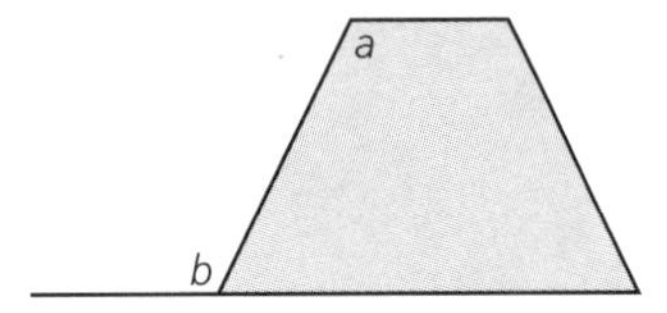

What is the size of angle b? (1)

50°	130°	150°	230°	120°
A	B	C	D	E

20 When these numbers are written in order of increasing size, which will be in the middle? (1)

5.34	3.45	4.35	3.54	4.53
A	B	C	D	E

21 The sum of the masses of the 24 children in a class is 1320 kg.
What is the average mass of a child? (1)

55 kg	48 kg	45 kg	56 kg	60 kg
A	B	C	D	E

22 About one in every ten people is left-handed.
Approximately how many more right-handed people than left-handed people would you expect there to be in a theatre audience of 900 people? (1)

100 more	800 more	700 more	90 more	890 more
A	B	C	D	E

23 Amanda buys three chocolate bars costing 65p each and a cake bar costing 75p.
How much change will she receive from a £5 note? (1)

£2.70	£3.70	£2.30	£3.30	£2.35
A	B	C	D	E

24 The 25 pupils in a class collected data about the numbers of brothers and sisters they have.

number of brothers and sisters	number of pupils
0	5
1	7
2	9
3	3
4	1

The school has a party for all 25 pupils and all of their brothers and sisters.
How many children will there be at the party? (1)

30	35	43	63	68
A	B	C	D	E

25 Exactly five years ago, Ava was twice as old as her brother Robin.
Ava is now 11 years old.
How old is Robin now? (1)

3	6	8	10	16
A	B	C	D	E

26 The diagram shows a maze.

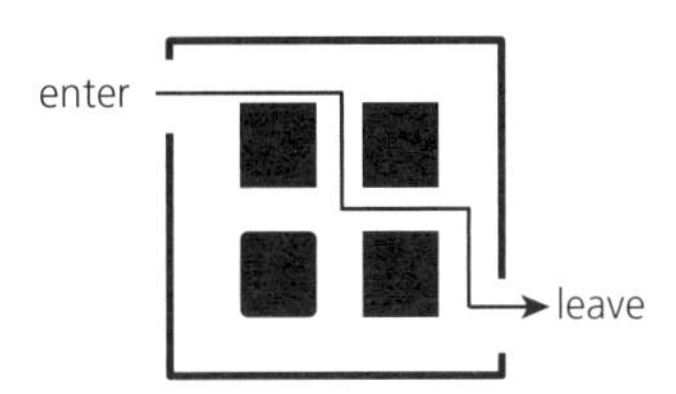

You are allowed to move in only two directions, *right* and *down* as you look at the plan.
One route through the maze is shown.
What is the total number of routes through the maze, *including the one shown*? (1)

3	4	5	6	7
A	B	C	D	E

27 For a school outing, the 328 pupils and 32 adults are to be transported by coach.
To hire a 50-seater coach costs £200, and to hire a 20-seater coach costs £80
What is the cheapest total transport cost of taking everyone on the outing? (1)

£1400	£1440	£1460	£1480	£1600
A	B	C	D	E

28 The table below shows the time Sarah spends on various activities during 24 hours.

activity	sleeping	eating	working	relaxing	travelling
time (hours)	$9\frac{1}{2}$	$1\frac{3}{4}$	7		$1\frac{1}{2}$

How long does Sarah spend relaxing? (1)

$3\frac{3}{4}$ hours	4 hours	$4\frac{1}{4}$ hours	$4\frac{1}{2}$ hours	$4\frac{3}{4}$ hours
A	B	C	D	E

29 Tim walks, on average, 3 km every day.

What is the best estimate of the total distance Tim walks in a year? (1)

500 km	1000 km	1500 km	2000 km	2500 km
A	B	C	D	E

30 Which of the following is the largest? (1)

4%	0.45	0.405	42%	$\frac{4}{5}$
A	B	C	D	E

31 The ratio of dogs to cats at a pet rescue centre is 5:3

There are 18 cats at the rescue centre.

How many dogs are there? (1)

90	20	25	30	45
A	B	C	D	E

32 Amber's school trip to France will cost exactly £1200

So far, Amber has £640 in the bank and her savings jar contains 138 one pound coins.

How much more does Amber need to save? (1)

£522	£698	£422	£432	£778
A	B	C	D	E

33 How many of the shapes below have no parallel sides? (1)

2	3	4	5	6
A	B	C	D	E

34 The area of a rectangle, with whole centimetre side lengths, is 24 cm^2.

Which of the following could *not* be the perimeter of the rectangle? (1)

20 cm	22 cm	26 cm	28 cm	50 cm
A	B	C	D	E

35 A fair spinner is shown below.

Which one of the following statements is true? (1)

A The spinner is most likely to land on grey.

B The spinner is least likely to land on white.

C If the spinner is spun ten times, you would expect it to land on white about six times.

D The spinner has a more than even chance of landing on white.

E The spinner is twice as likely to land on grey than to land on black.

36 Andy, Barbara and Clare start with 20 marbles each.

In the first round, Andy wins five marbles from Barbara, Barbara loses seven marbles to Clare and Clare wins six from Andy.

In the second round, Andy loses 14 marbles to Barbara, Barbara wins eight from Clare and Clare loses four to Andy.

Which of the following represents the numbers of marbles each player has at the end of round two? (1)

A9, B30, C21	A11, B22, C27	A16, B17, C27	A11, B33, C16	A12, B31, C17
A	B	C	D	E

37 A plan of the school grounds is drawn to a scale of 1:500

On the plan, the distance between two oak trees is 4 cm.

How far apart are the real trees? (1)

200 m	12.5 m	125 m	20 m	2 m
A	B	C	D	E

38 Which of the following gives a different result from all of the others? (1)

a third of 18	$4 \times 1\frac{1}{2}$	30×0.2	$1 + 2 \times 2$	$\frac{2}{3}$ of 9
A	B	C	D	E

39 The table shows the proportions of different types of tree in a wood.

type of tree	ash	beech	chestnut	oak
proportion	28%	14%		44%

There are 56 ash trees in the wood.

How many chestnut trees are there? (1)

20	14	24	56	28
A	B	C	D	E

40 $a - 2b = 5c$

Which of the following is correct? (1)

$a + 5c = 2b$	$5c + 2b = a$	$2a - 4b = 5c$	$2b - a = 5c$	$5c = a + 2b$
A	B	C	D	E

41 Madison has two identical baking trays that can each make 12 muffins at a time.

Madison has an order for 200 muffins.

She fills *both* baking trays each time before she puts them in the oven, until she has made at least 200 muffins.

How many muffins will she have left over when she has delivered the order of 200? (1)

14	16	12	10	18
A	B	C	D	E

42 A school badge costs £4.99

Half of the 400 pupils at Oaktree School buy a badge.

How much money does the school take for the badges? (1)

£1000	£499	£998	£999	£99.80
A	B	C	D	E

43 The *perimeter* of the shaded square is 12 cm.

What is the *area* of the large square? (1)

36 cm^2	24 cm^2	48 cm^2	64 cm^2	18 cm^2
A	B	C	D	E

44 Hamish is being measured for a kilt. The distance round his waist is 30 inches.

Which of the following is the closest to his waist measurement in centimetres? (1)

60 cm	90 cm	120 cm	75 cm	45 cm
A	B	C	D	E

45 A coffee costs c pence and a muffin costs m pence.

A group of four friends have a coffee and muffin each and then two of them have a second coffee and one of them has a second muffin.

What is the total cost, in pence, of the coffees and muffins? (1)

$4c + 5m$	$5c + 4m$	$6c + 4m$	$6c + 5m$	$5c + 6m$
A	B	C	D	E

46 Which of the following has the greatest value? (1)

40% of 20	20% of 40	80% of 10	a tenth of 80	8.05
A	B	C	D	E

47 James' walking pace distance is 90 cm and Jenny's walking pace distance is 80 cm.

They set off together and walk the distance between two trees.

James walks 72 paces.

How many more, or fewer, paces does Jenny walk than James? (1)

11 more	10 fewer	10 more	9 fewer	9 more
A	B	C	D	E

48 Sandy has a number machine that subtracts 4, multiplies by 5 and finally adds 3

What was the input if the output is 68? (1)

13	17	15	19	16
A	B	C	D	E

49 How many square numbers are there less than 200? (1)

15	14	13	12	11
A	B	C	D	E

50 In the wall of bricks shown below, the number on a brick is the sum of the numbers on the two bricks supporting it.

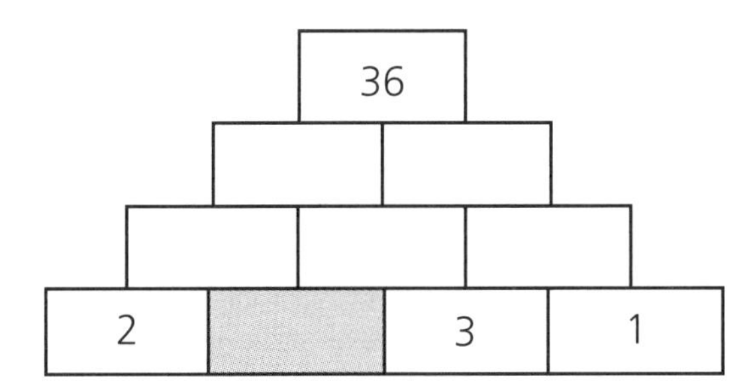

What number is on the shaded brick? (1)

10	8	6	4	2
A	B	C	D	E

Paper 4

Test time: 50 minutes

Write your answer on the answer line or circle the correct answer where asked to do so.

1 Write the number forty-five million, thirty-six thousand and eight in figures. (1)

____

2 What is the value of the 7 in 470,000? (1)

____

3 How many sixes are there in 666? (1)

____

4 The machine below multiplies by five and then subtracts seven.

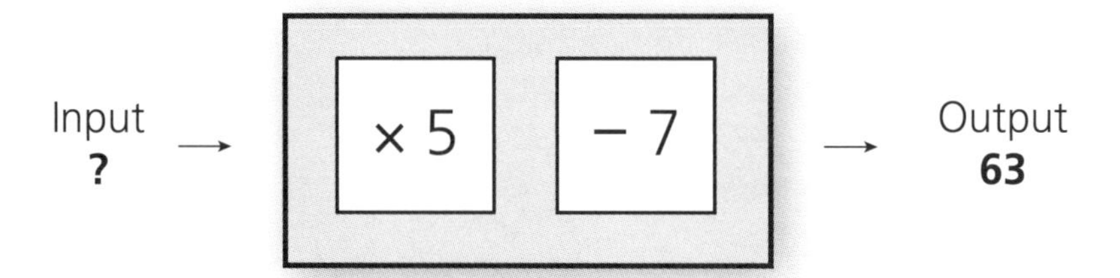

What number was put in? (1)

____

5 An egg box holds half a dozen eggs.
Mrs Brown needs 54 eggs for her baking.
How many boxes of eggs should she buy? (1)

____

6 The pictogram below shows the results of a survey into the numbers of dogs and cats owned by the pupils in a class.

One symbol represents two pets.
What is the total number of dogs and cats owned by the pupils? (1)

____

7 St Bernard's school has 450 pupils.

On Friday, 47 pupils were absent with flu and during the day another 137 pupils felt unwell and were sent home.

How many pupils were at school when the bell rang for the end of the school day? (1)

____

Questions 8 to 10 are about the lunches bought by four friends.
Each friend could choose a maximum of one of each of the items listed.

Item	Price
Soup	£2.05
Sandwich	£1.10
Crisps	£0.60
Juice	£1.15
Muffin	£0.75

8 Maya had a bowl of soup, a sandwich and a muffin.
How much did Maya spend? (1)

____

9 Max had just two items at a total cost of £2.80
Which two items did Max have? (1)

____

10 Cheryl paid for her lunch with a £10 note and received £4.95 in change.
How many items did Cheryl have? (1)

____

Questions 11 to 14 are about the measuring containers A and B below, containing lemonade.

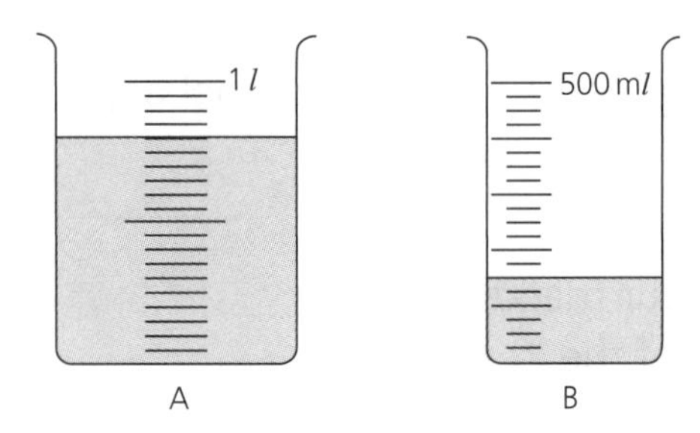

11 The volume of lemonade in container **A** is 800 ml.
Write this as a fraction of a litre in its simplest form (lowest terms). (1)

____

12 What is the volume of lemonade, *in millilitres*, in container **B**? (1)

____

13 How many 160 ml glasses could be filled with the lemonade in container **A**? (1)

____

14 Two litres of lemonade costs £3.20
What is the value of the lemonade in container **A**? (1)

____

Questions 15 to 20 are about the centimetre square grid shown here.

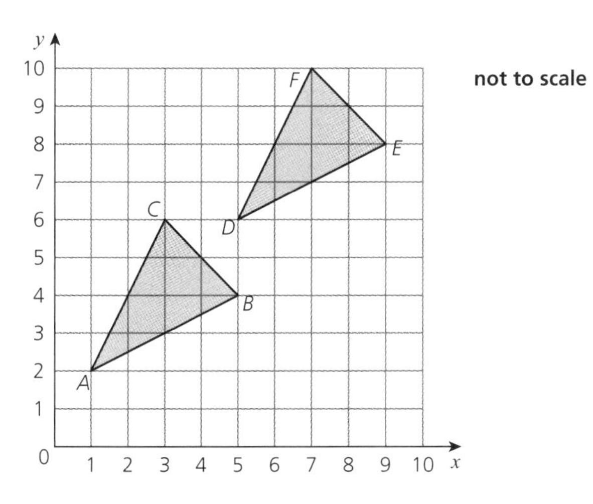

15 Write down the co-ordinates of the point A. (1)

____

16 Write down the co-ordinates of the point that is exactly half way between (1, 2) and (9, 4). (1)

____

17 What type of triangle is triangle ABC? (1)

____

18 What is the area of triangle ABC? (1)

____

19 What word describes the transformation that would map triangle ABC onto triangle DEF? (1)

____

20 What type of angle is angle BCA? (1)

____

21 The temperature was 5 °C yesterday and today it is seven degrees cooler.
What is the temperature today? (1)

____

22 What is the next cube number after 64? (1)

____

23 How many lines of symmetry does this shape have? (1)

____

24 Which of the fractions below has the smallest value? (1)

$\frac{3}{8}$ $\frac{1}{3}$ $\frac{2}{5}$ $\frac{4}{9}$ $\frac{4}{7}$

____

25 Which *two* of the numbers below add to make a prime number? (1)

21 14 19 2 37

____

26 Asha has a favourite number.
She adds 3 to her favourite number and then multiplies by 3
The result is 21
What is Asha's favourite number? (1)

____

27 A hotel buys 60 litres of milk, in 2-litre bottles, every day.
A 2-litre bottle costs £1.20
How much does the hotel spend on milk in a 30-day month? (1)

____

28 A piece of wire is bent to form a regular hexagon with sides of length 8 cm.

The wire is straightened out and then bent again to form a square.
What is the length of the side of the square? (1)

29 The distance from Appleford to Bankton is 8 kilometres (5 miles).
Crinkly is 40 miles from Appleford.
Simon drives from his home in Bankton to Crinkly, passing through Appleford.
How many kilometres does he drive? (1)

30 Amelia helps in her father's shop for one and a quarter hours each weekday after school, and for 5 hours on Saturday.
If she earns £4 per hour, how much will Amelia earn in a week? (1)

31 The plan of a game board is drawn to a scale of 1 cm to represent 8 cm.

The plan measures 4 cm by 5.5 cm.

What is the total area of the grey squares on the real board? (1)

32 Which two numbers, both less than 20, have a product of 187? (1)

33 Simon collects stamps.
British stamps make up approximately one-ninth of his collection.
He has 111 British stamps.
Approximately how many stamps (to the nearest 50), are there in Simon's collection? (1)

34 The regular hexagon is drawn on an isometric dotted grid.

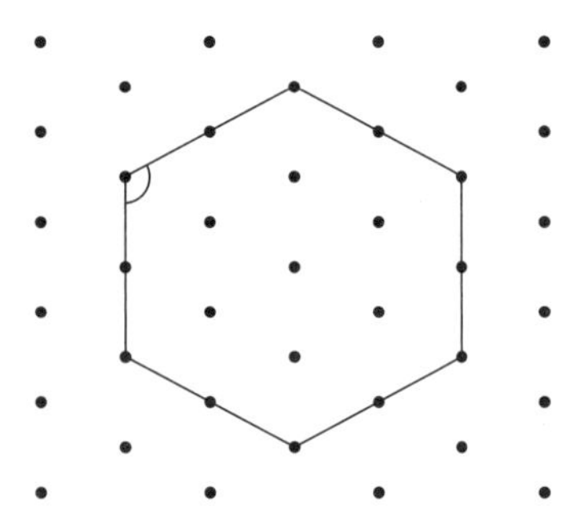

What is the size of one interior angle of a regular hexagon? **(1)**

____

35 Alya plants 144 identical seeds.
Eight-ninths of the seeds grow into plants.
How many of the seeds do *not* grow into plants? **(1)**

____

36 The ratio of swans to ducks on a pond is 2:15
There are six swans.
How many more ducks are there than swans? **(1)**

____

37 Louise scored the following numbers of runs in her last five cricket matches.

17 0 0 43 0

What is her median score? **(1)**

____

38 Which of the following solid shapes has the largest number of faces?
Circle the correct answer. **(1)**

tetrahedron pentagonal pyramid hexagonal pyramid cube

39 The diagram shows the plan of Sarah's bedroom floor.

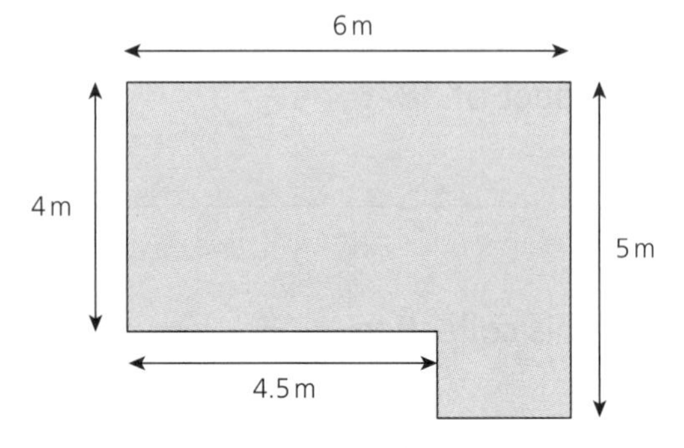

What is the area of the floor? **(1)**

____

40 $3x - 8 = x + 4$
What is the value of x? (1)

____

41 The table shows information about the 24 pupils in a class.

do not like haggis	4	5
like haggis	6	8
	boys	girls

What fraction of the pupils like haggis? (1)

____

42 A shirt originally priced at £28 is reduced by 40% in a sale.
What is the sale price? (1)

____

43 The two-digit number 43 has a digit sum of 7 because $4 + 3 = 7$
What is the smallest *three-digit* number that has a digit sum of 7? (1)

____

44 By how much is *a third of six* larger than *a sixth of three*? (1)

____

45 Ahmed's height is a cm and he is growing by 1 cm each month.
Barbara's height is 130 cm and she is growing by b cm each month.
At the end of six months, Ahmed is the taller. Which of the following expressions describes the difference between their heights?
Circle the correct answer. (1)

$a + 6 - 130 + 6b$ $a + 6 - 130 - 6b$ $a - 124 + 6b$

46 One angle of an isosceles trapezium is 135°.
What size is the largest of the other three angles? (1)

____

47 What is the sum of the first five multiples of 6? (6 is the first multiple of 6) (1)

____

48 The diagram shows the first three patterns in a sequence

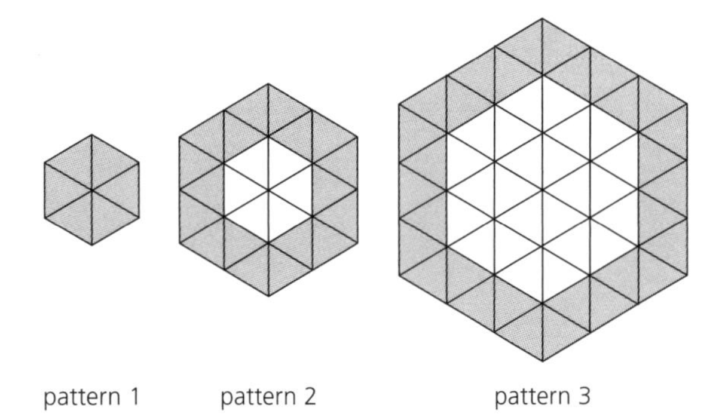

How many grey triangles will there be in pattern number 4? **(1)**

____

49 a is two-thirds of b.

One of the following equations is incorrect.

Circle the incorrect equation. **(1)**

$3a = 2b$ $\qquad \frac{a}{b} = \frac{2}{3}$ $\qquad \frac{3a}{b} = 2$ $\qquad 3b = 2a$ $\qquad b = \frac{3a}{2}$

50 The shape is made from two equilateral triangles and two squares.

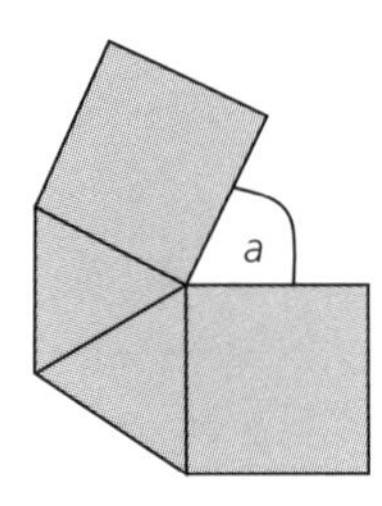

What is the size of angle a? **(1)**

____

Answers

All the references in the boxes below refer to the *11+ Mathematics Revision Guide* (ISBN: 9781471849213) so you know exactly where to find out more about the question and your answer.

PAPER 1

1 C **3** M, A and T have a vertical line of symmetry only; H has two lines of symmetry; S has rotation symmetry only (1)

See pages 82–83.

2 B **21p** $200-95=105$; $105\div5=21$ (1)

See pages 50–51.

3 D **2, 23, 37** 39, 27, 69 and 21 are not prime; all divide by 3 (1)

See pages 20–21.

4 C **33** $47+37=84$; $23+28=51$; $84-51=33$; adding vertical differences $24+9=33$ is quicker (1)

See pages 134–135.

5 B **7** $23+5=28$; $28\div4=7$ (1)

See pages 124–125.

6 C **1833** One way: $40\times47=1880$; $1880-47=1833$ (1)

See pages 34–35.

7 A **2** In order: 0, 1, 3, 6; the median is the middle value; in this case, the mean of the middle two (1)

See pages 146–147.

8 D **17.5 cm^2** 3.5×5; $3.5\times10=35$ and then $35\div2=17.5$ is probably easier (1)

See pages 94–95.

9 B **12** Factors of 12 are 1, 2, 3, 4, 6, 12; factors of 10 are 1, 2, 5, 10; factors of 16 are 1, 2, 4, 8, 16; factors of 19 are 1, 19; factors of 22 are 1, 11, 22 (1)

See pages 18–19.

10 B **£11.90 £8.10** $2\times595=1190$; $2000-1190=810$ (1)

See pages 50–51.

11 D **7.6** $70.3\div18.5=3.8$; $140.6\div18.5=7.6$ (1)

12 D **8** Working backwards: $20+4=24$; $24\div3=8$ (1)

See pages 122–123.

13 E **£5.40** $11-4=7$; $7\times20=140$; £4 + £1.40 = £5.40 (1)

See pages 50–51.

14 B **100** Page approx. 30 cm × 20 cm; coin diameter approx. 2.5 cm; approx. 12 coins down, 8 across (1)

See pages 14–17.

15 D **5** $14\div7=2$; $56\div7=8$; $91\div7=13$; $28\div7=4$; $63\div7=9$ (1)

See pages 36–37.

16 C 6 Reasoning: $2x-4=x+2; x=6$ (1)

See pages 124–125.

17 D 7 Dogs $3\frac{1}{2}$ symbols more; each symbol represents two pets; $2\times3\frac{1}{2}=7$ (1)

See pages 136–137.

18 D 1°C $14-18={}^{-}4; {}^{-}4+5=1$ (1)

See pages 26–27.

19 D 6 Making an organised list: 345, 354, 435, 453, 534, 543 (1)

20 E $15\frac{1}{2}$ $62\div2=31; 31\div2=15\frac{1}{2}$ (1)

See pages 58–59.

21 C 5 The numbers are: 14, 23, 32, 41 and 50 (1)

22 C 180 $123+39+18=180$ (1)

See pages 30–31.

23 D £48.94 £53.19 − £4.25 = £48.94 (1)

See pages 50–51.

24 B 6 £5.00 − £2.48 = £2.52; divide by factors of 42: $252\div6=42; 42\div7=6$ (1)

See pages 50–51.

25 E (1.6, 1.2) Each little division on each axis represents 0.2 (1)

See pages 72–73.

26 E E2-S2-E2-N1-E2 Immediately ignore any option with a W (1)

See pages 110–111.

27 A £5.40 6 apples cost £1.80 (half of £3.60); 18 apples cost £5.40 (three times £1.80) (1)

See pages 50–51.

28 D 3.04 In order of increasing size, the numbers are: 2.9, 2.94, 2.95, **3.04**, 3.1 (1)

See pages 12–13.

29 C 150 cm 1 foot is approximately 30 cm; $5\times30=150$ (1)

See pages 72–73.

30 D 8 $a+4=2(a-2); a+4=2a-4; 8=a$ ('intuition' or 'guess and check') (1)

See pages 74–75.

31 B 0 Multiplication before addition and subtraction; $8+7-15=0$ (1)

See pages 28–29.

32 D 40 cm The same perimeter as a square of side 10 cm (1)

See pages 92–93.

33 D 31 $(2\times4)+(3\times6)+5=8+18+5$ (1)

See pages 126–127.

34 E 56, 81 7×8 and 9×9 (1)

35 A **3.023** In order of increasing size, the numbers are: 2.303, 2.33, **3.023**, 3.203 3.22 (1)

See pages 56–57.

36 E **35%** $\frac{140}{400}=\frac{7}{20}=\frac{35}{100}$; or divide by 2 and then by 2 again (1)

See pages 54–55.

37 B $\frac{4}{11}$ 11 small triangles in half of hexagon, so 22 in total; 8 small triangles shaded; $\frac{8}{22}=\frac{8}{11}$ (1)

See pages 58–59.

38 D $\frac{3}{8}$ 3 white counters; 8 counters in total; 3 out of 8 (1)

See pages 156–157.

39 D **3.45** The third figure to right of the point is 5, so round up (1)

See pages 14–17.

40 D **2500** Approximately 50×50 (1)

See pages 14–17.

41 D **36 minutes** 08:37 to 09:00 is 23 minutes; $23+13=36$ (1)

See pages 74–75.

42 B $\frac{1}{6}$ 12 slices in total; Bella has eaten 2; $\frac{2}{12}=\frac{1}{6}$ (1)

See pages 58–59.

43 B **45.4** Look at the 4th significant figure; it is 4, so round down (1)

See pages 14–17.

44 C **16** The sequence of square numbers: 1, 4, 9, 16 (1)

See pages 124–125 and 130–131.

45 D **isosceles** The third angle is 54° ($180-72=108$; $108-54=54$) (1)

See pages 108–109.

46 D **£72** 10% is £40; 1% is £4; 8% is £32 (8×£4); 18% is £72 (£40+£32) (1)

See pages 62–63.

47 E **6** The only shape that does not have rotational symmetry of order 2 is the isosceles trapezium (third from left) (1)

See pages 82–83.

48 D **72 cm** Diameter 24 cm (twice radius); circumference approx. 3 times diameter (1)

See pages 90–91.

49 B **101.57** To the right of the point, $49+8=57$; to the left of the point, $12+89=101$ (1)

See pages 30–31.

50 D **5** There are nine 'shares' in total; there are five sweets in each share; Bill has one more 'share' than Ben (1)

See pages 46–47.

PAPER 2

1 E **29** $5+10+6+8=29$ (1)

See pages 138–139.

2 B **4** One-sixth are aged under 16; $24 \div 6=4$ (1)

See pages 58–59.

3 C **350 g** 1 kg 50 g is 1050 g; $1050 \div 3=350$ (1)

See pages 72–73.

4 D **S** B has one line of symmetry; H, O and X each have two lines of symmetry, and rotational symmetry order 2 (1)

See pages 82–83.

5 E **8 cm** 1 length + 1 width is 12 cm; 8 cm long and 4 cm wide; algebraic solution x wide, $2x$ long; $6x=24$; $x=4$ (1)

See pages 92–93.

6 B **3570** 5 hundreds; others are units, hundredths, tens, tenths (1)

See pages 12–13.

7 D **13** $0+4+6+3$; no goals were scored in 2 matches (1)

See pages 146–147.

8 C **20p** $2 \times 12=24$; $480 \div 24=20$; dividing by factors (4 and then 6) may be easier (1)

See pages 36–37.

9 D **27** One-third are male; $9 \times 3=27$ (1)

See pages 48–49.

10 C **4** Top row $10-6-3=1$; middle column $14-9-1=4$ (1)
11 E **6** $2 \times 45=90$; $210-90=120$; $120 \div 20=6$ (1)

See pages 50–51.

12 B **(7, 6)** From (6, 2): right 1, up 4 (1)

See pages 112–113.

13 E **0.6 litres** $200 \times 7=1400$; $2000-1400=600$; 600 ml = 0.6 l (1)

See pages 102–103.

14 B **a fifth** $\frac{3}{5}$ of cake left; Mhairi eats $\frac{1}{5}$ (a third of $\frac{3}{5}$) (1)

See pages 58–59.

15 D **24** $24 \div 6=4$; $24 \div 8=3$ (1)

See pages 36–37.

16 E **25** $\frac{5}{8}$ have no illustrations; $40 \div 8=5$; $5 \times 5=25$ (1)

See pages 48–49 and 58–59.

17 B $4\frac{1}{2}$	$23-5=18$; $18\div4=4\frac{1}{2}$	(1)

See pages 112–113.

18 E **10.75**	The figure in the third decimal place is 5, so round up	(1)

See pages 14–17.

19 C **(regular pentagon)**	C has five lines of symmetry, A has four, D has three and B and E each have two	(1)

See pages 80–83.

20 B **£36.00**	One turn on each has total cost £12; $3\times12=36$; this is easier than doing three multiplications	(1)

See pages 50–51.

21 E $13-y$	Rosie is y years older than Samantha	(1)

See pages 126–127.

22 A **84**	'Groups' of 7 (1 adult, 6 children); $104-6=98$ (people); $98\div7=14$; 14 adults; $98-14=84$ children	(1)

See pages 46–47.

23 C **75%**	One-quarter eaten; three-quarters left	(1)

See pages 54–55.

24 B **£8.40**	80% of original price; 10% is £1.05; 80% is $8\times$£1.05	(1)

See pages 64–65.

25 A **0.9 kg**	1.4 kg shown; $1400-500=900$; 900 g = 0.9 kg	(1)

See pages 72–73.

26 E **16 cm**	$3+3+5+5$	(1)

See pages 92–93.

27 D **84**	36, 54, 72 and 102 all divide by 6; $84\div6=14$; $84\div7=12$	(1)

See pages 36–37.

28 C **9**	Work backwards: $15\times2=30$; $30+6=36$; $36\div4=9$	(1)

See pages 124–125.

29 A **20**	In order: 14, 17, 17, 20, 22, 31, 40; middle number 20	(1)

See pages 146–147.

30 B **40 cm**	$24\times2.5=60$; $100-60=40$	(1)

See pages 72–73.

31 A $6a+5b$	6 apples cost $6\times a$ pence; 5 bananas cost $5\times b$ pence	(1)

See pages 126–127.

32 B	There are 9 green marbles $(20-4-7)$; $\frac{9}{20}$ is a less than even chance, so statement B is not true	(1)

See pages 156–157.

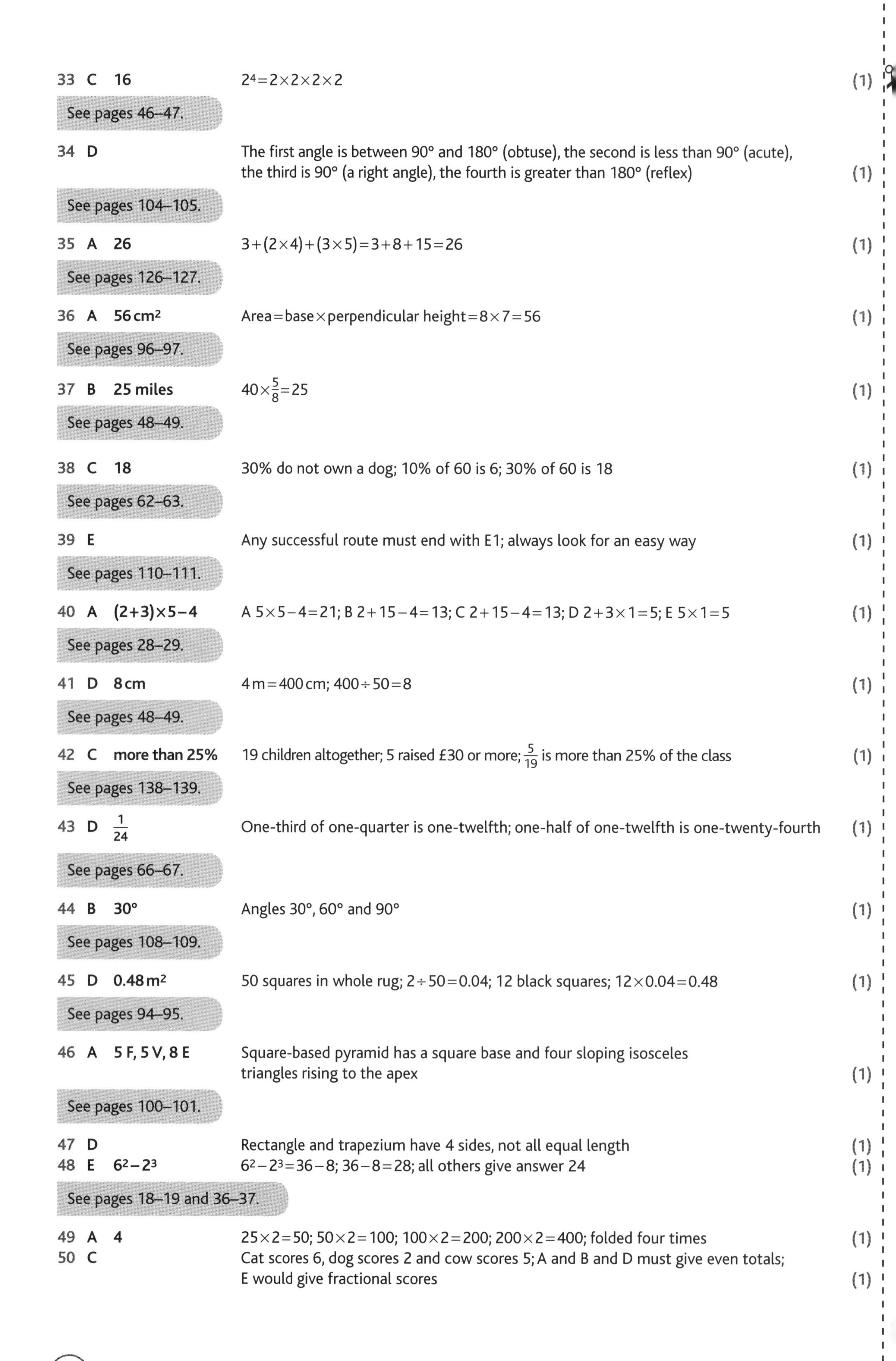

33 C 16 — $2^4 = 2 \times 2 \times 2 \times 2$ (1)

See pages 46–47.

34 D — The first angle is between 90° and 180° (obtuse), the second is less than 90° (acute), the third is 90° (a right angle), the fourth is greater than 180° (reflex) (1)

See pages 104–105.

35 A 26 — $3 + (2 \times 4) + (3 \times 5) = 3 + 8 + 15 = 26$ (1)

See pages 126–127.

36 A 56 cm² — Area = base × perpendicular height $= 8 \times 7 = 56$ (1)

See pages 96–97.

37 B 25 miles — $40 \times \frac{5}{8} = 25$ (1)

See pages 48–49.

38 C 18 — 30% do not own a dog; 10% of 60 is 6; 30% of 60 is 18 (1)

See pages 62–63.

39 E — Any successful route must end with E1; always look for an easy way (1)

See pages 110–111.

40 A $(2+3) \times 5 - 4$ — A $5 \times 5 - 4 = 21$; B $2 + 15 - 4 = 13$; C $2 + 15 - 4 = 13$; D $2 + 3 \times 1 = 5$; E $5 \times 1 = 5$ (1)

See pages 28–29.

41 D 8 cm — 4 m = 400 cm; $400 \div 50 = 8$ (1)

See pages 48–49.

42 C more than 25% — 19 children altogether; 5 raised £30 or more; $\frac{5}{19}$ is more than 25% of the class (1)

See pages 138–139.

43 D $\frac{1}{24}$ — One-third of one-quarter is one-twelfth; one-half of one-twelfth is one-twenty-fourth (1)

See pages 66–67.

44 B 30° — Angles 30°, 60° and 90° (1)

See pages 108–109.

45 D 0.48 m² — 50 squares in whole rug; $2 \div 50 = 0.04$; 12 black squares; $12 \times 0.04 = 0.48$ (1)

See pages 94–95.

46 A 5 F, 5 V, 8 E — Square-based pyramid has a square base and four sloping isosceles triangles rising to the apex (1)

See pages 100–101.

47 D — Rectangle and trapezium have 4 sides, not all equal length (1)

48 E $6^2 - 2^3$ — $6^2 - 2^3 = 36 - 8$; $36 - 8 = 28$; all others give answer 24 (1)

See pages 18–19 and 36–37.

49 A 4 — $25 \times 2 = 50$; $50 \times 2 = 100$; $100 \times 2 = 200$; $200 \times 2 = 400$; folded four times (1)

50 C — Cat scores 6, dog scores 2 and cow scores 5; A and B and D must give even totals; E would give fractional scores (1)

PAPER 3

1 D OHO — A, B and C have no lines of symmetry; E has a vertical line of symmetry only (1)

See pages 82–83.

2 C 7 — There are 12 boys ($5+3+4$); there are 18 girls ($12+6$); $18-6-5=7$ (1)

See pages 134–135.

3 A £0 — Exactly the same cost; compare smaller amount such as 1500 g; $2\times£2.40=£4.80$; $3\times£1.60=£4.80$ (1)

4 B 12 and 48 — Numbers in each row halve going from left to right; numbers in each column halve going down the table (1)

See pages 124–125.

5 B 1:2000 — 10 cm to 20 000 cm; divide both numbers by 10 to give 1 cm to represent 2000 cm (1)

See pages 48–49.

6 E — There are 24 plants ($2+4+8+7+3$); A, C and D are definitely false, B *could* be true; only E *must* be true (1)

See pages 138–139.

7 D 20:45 — Add 12 hours (1)

See pages 74–75.

8 A 60° — Imagine an equilateral triangle with angle *a* at one vertex (1)

See pages 104–105.

9 D 63 — $63=7\times9$ (1)

See pages 20–21.

10 C $\frac{1}{10}$ — $\frac{200}{2000}=\frac{1}{10}$ (1)

See pages 58–59 and 72–73.

11 C 305 305 — Eliminate any choice without 5 in the units place first; the numbers of thousands and units are the same (1)

See pages 12–13.

12 C 13 — Guess and check or use algebra ($2m-7=m+6$) (1)

See pages 124–125.

13 B *IJ* (7, 2) (3, 6) — *A* and *E* are parallel to *AB*; *C* and *D* are not parallel or perpendicular to *AB* (1)

See pages 109–110.

14 D 2.83 — Each division on the scale represents 0.02; the arrow points to half way between 2.82 and 2.84 (1)

See pages 72–73.

15 E $\frac{3}{5}$ — Total 65 children; $\frac{39}{65}$ simplifies by dividing numerator and denominator by 13 (1)

See pages 58–59.

16 C 3 — First, second and fourth are congruent to P (1)

See pages 78–79.

17	A		Two sides the same length; it may help to turn the page round	(1)

See pages 106–107.

18	A	**(3.4, 2.6)**	Each small division represents 0.2; horizontal two divisions (0.4) beyond 3 so 3.4; vertical six divisions (0.6) beyond 2 so 2.6	(1)

See pages 72–73.

19	B	**130°**	Top and bottom of isosceles trapezium are parallel; *a* and *b* are alternate angles	(1)

See pages 86–87.

20	C	**4.35**	In order: 3.45, 3.54, **4.35**, 4.53, 5.34	(1)

See pages 56–57.

21	A	**55 kg**	$1320 \div 24$; divide by factors of 24, e.g. $1320 \div 4 = 330$; $330 \div 3 = 110$; $110 \div 2 = 55$	(1)

See pages 146–147.

22	C	**700 more**	$900 \div 10 = 90$; 90 left-handed; 810 right-handed; $810 - 90 = 720$ and 700 is closest to 720	(1)

See pages 48–49.

23	C	**£2.30**	Look for an easy way: $2 \times 65 = 130$; $65 + 75 = 140$; $130 + 140 = 270$; $500 - 270 = 230$	(1)

See pages 50–51.

24	D	**63**	Total 38 brothers and sisters $(0 + 7 + 18 + 9 + 4)$; $38 + 25$	(1)

See pages 146–147.

25	C	**8**	Five years ago Ava was six and Robin was three; Robin is now eight	(1)

See pages 126–127.

26	D	**6**	Three routes going above top LH square; two routes going above bottom LH square; one route going below bottom LH square	(1)
27	B	**£1440**	The coaches have the same cost per person; any combination of coaches that does not have empty seats has the same cost	(1)

See pages 50–51.

28	C	**$4\frac{1}{4}$ hours**	Look for the simplest way: $9\frac{1}{2} + 1\frac{1}{2} = 11$; $11 + 7 = 18$; $24 - 18 = 6$; $6 - 1\frac{3}{4} = 4\frac{1}{4}$	(1)

See pages 58–59 and 74–75.

29	B	**1000 km**	Approximate 365×3 to 370×3 or even 400×3 (too large); $400 \times 3 = 1200$; 1000 is closest to 1200	(1)

See pages 14–17 and 76–77.

30	E	$\frac{4}{5}$	Probably easiest to convert all to decimals: A 0.04; B 0.45; C 0.405; D 0.42; E 0.8	(1)

See pages 54–55.

31	D	**30**	Equivalent ratio to 5 : 3 is 30 : 18 (both number $\times$ 6)	(1)

See pages 46–47.

32	C	**£422**	$640 + 138 = 778$; $1200 - 778 = 422$	(1)

See pages 50–51.

33	B	**3**	Regular pentagon, regular heptagon and triangle	(1)

See pages 88–89.

34	C	**26 cm**	1×24 gives perimeter 50 (2×25); 2×12 gives perimeter 28; 3×8 gives perimeter 22; 4×6 gives perimeter 20 (2×10)	(1)

See pages 92–93.

35	E		Five sections: two grey, two white, one black; black probability $\frac{1}{5}$; grey probability $\frac{2}{5}$; white probability $\frac{2}{5}$	(1)

See pages 156–157.

36	A	**A9, B30, C21**	Since all the choices have a different number for Barbara, just check how she gets on ($20-5-7+14+8=30$)	(1)
37	D	**20 m**	$500 \times 4 = 2000$; 2000 cm is 20 m	(1)

See pages 48–49.

38	D	**1+2×2**	$1+2 \times 2 = 5$; all other choices have the answer 6	(1)

See pages 58–59 and 92–93.

39	E	**28**	$28+14+44=86$; $100-86=14$; chestnut trees 14%; ash trees 28% (56 trees) so 28 ($56 \div 2$) chestnut trees	(1)

See pages 48–49.

40	B	**$5c+2b=a$**	$5c=a-2b$ (subtract $2b$ from each side) then swap sides to get the original equation	(1)

See pages 126–127.

41	B	**16**	24 muffins in each batch; multiples of 24 are 48, 72, 96, 120, 144, 168, 192, 216; $216-200=16$	(1)

See pages 36–39.

42	C	**£998**	200 pupils buy badges; $200 \times £5 = £1000$; $200 \times 1p = £2$; $£1000 - £2 = £998$	(1)

See pages 24–25.

43	A	**36 cm²**	Side of shaded square is 3 cm ($12 \div 4$); side of large square is 6 cm; $6 \times 6 = 36$	(1)

See pages 92–95.

44	D	**75 cm**	12 inches is approximately 30 cm; 30 inches is $2\frac{1}{2} \times 30$ cm	(1)

See pages 72–73.

45	D	**$6c+5m$**	6 coffees $(4+2)$ is $6c$; 5 muffins $(4+1)$ is $5m$	(1)

See pages 126–127.

46	E	**8.05**	All other options have value 8	(1)

See pages 58–59 and 62–63.

47	E	**9 more**	$72 \times 90 = 6480$; $6480 \div 80 = 81$; Jenny 81 paces; $81-72=9$	(1)
48	B	**17**	Work backwards: $68-3=65$; $65 \div 5 = 13$; $13+4=17$	(1)

See pages 122–123.

49	B	**14**	$1^2=1$; $2^2=4$, etc; $12^2=144$; $13^2=169$; $14^2=196$	(1)

See pages 18–19.

50	B	**8**	Trial and improvement (guess and check)	(1)

PAPER 4

1 **45,036,008** It may help to write the number down starting on the right with the 8 units (1)

See pages 12–13.

2 **70,000** M HTh TTh Th H T U (1)

See pages 12–13.

3 **111** $666 \div 6 = 111$ (1)

See pages 36–37.

4 **14** Work backwards: $63 + 7 = 70$; $70 \div 5 = 14$ (1)

See pages 122–123.

5 **9** 'Half a dozen' is 6; $54 \div 6 = 9$ (1)

See pages 36–37.

6 **23** There are $11\frac{1}{2}$ symbols; each symbol represents two pets (1)

See pages 136–137.

7 **266** $450 - 47 = 403$; $403 - 137 = 266$; it may be easier to add 47 and 137 and then subtract (1)

See pages 24–25 and 30–31.

8 **£3.90** £2.05 + £1.10 + £0.75 (1)

See pages 50–51.

9 **soup and muffin** £2.05 + £0.75 (1)

See pages 50–51.

10 **4** £10.00 − £4.95 = £5.05; one of each gives total cost £5.65; the four items are soup, sandwich, juice and muffin (1)

11 $\frac{4}{5}$ 1000 ml in one litre; $\frac{800}{1000}$ simplifies to $\frac{8}{10}$ and then $\frac{4}{5}$ (1)

See pages 102–103.

12 **150 ml** Each 'long' division represents 100 ml; each 'short' division represents 25 ml (1)

See pages 72–73.

13 **5** $800 \div 160 = 5$; divide by factors $80 \div 4 = 20$ and then $20 \div 4 = 5$ (1)

See pages 36–37.

14 **£1.28** 1 litre costs £1.60; 100 ml costs 16p; $8 \times 16 = 128$ (1)

See pages 50–51.

15 **(1, 2)** x line 1; y line 2 (1)

See pages 114–115.

16 **(5, 3)** Find mean of co-ordinate numbers; $(1 + 9) \div 2$; $(2 + 4) \div 2$ (1)

17 **isosceles** Two sides equal: AC and AB are both diagonals of 4×2 rectangles (1)

See pages 106–107.

18 **6 cm²** Subtract areas of three triangles from area of 4 cm square; $16 - 4 - 4 - 2$; or re-arrange bits of cm squares (1)

See pages 96–97.

19 **translation** Move each point 4 units to the right, and 4 units up (1)

See pages 114–115.

20 **acute** Angle less than 90° (1)

See pages 104–105.

21 **$^{-}2$ °C** $5-7={}^{-}2$ (1)

See pages 26–27.

22 **125** $64=4^3$; $5^3=125$ ($5\times5\times5$) (1)

See pages 18–19.

23 **2** Two lines of symmetry (1)

See pages 82–83.

24 **$\frac{1}{3}$** $\frac{3}{8}$ is more than $\frac{3}{9}\left(\frac{1}{3}\right)$; $\frac{2}{5}$ is more than $\frac{2}{6}\left(\frac{1}{3}\right)$; $\frac{4}{9}$ is more than $\frac{3}{9}\left(\frac{1}{3}\right)$ and $\frac{4}{7}$ is more than $\frac{1}{2}$ (1)

See pages 42–43 and 52–53.

25 **2 and 21** One number must be even and one odd; $2+21=23$ (1)

See pages 20–21.

26 **4** Work backwards: $21\div3=7$; $7-3=4$ (1)

See pages 124–125.

27 **£1080** 30 bottles a day; 900 bottles in a 30-day month; $900\times1=900$; $900\times0.20=180$; £900 + £180 = £1080 (1)

See pages 50–51 and 102–103.

28 **12 cm** Length of wire $6\times8=48$; $48\div4=12$ (1)

See pages 88–89 and 92–93.

29 **72 km** 40 miles is 64 km (8×8); $64+8=72$ (1)

See pages 72–73.

30 **£45** £4 per hour; £5 for $1\frac{1}{4}$ hours; £5 each weekday gives £5 × 5 = £25; £4 × 5 = £20 on Saturday; £25 + £20 = £45 (1)

See pages 50–51.

31 **640 cm^2** 88 squares (11×8); 40 grey squares; side of real square 4 cm (8×0.5); area of real square 16 cm^2; $40\times16=640$ (1)

See pages 94–95.

32 **11 and 17** Numbers end in 1 and 7 or 3 and 9; guess and check; $11\times17=187$ ($11\times10+11\times7$) (1)

See pages 38–39.

33 **1000** Total stamps $9\times111=999$; round to nearest 50 (1)

See pages 14–17 and 58–59.

34 **120°** Isometric grid; dots positioned as if vertices of equilateral triangles; $2\times60°$ (1)

See pages 88–89 and 108–109.

35	**16**	One-ninth do not grow; $144 \div 9 = 16$	(1)

See pages 58–59.

36	**39**	Equivalent ratio 6:45; there are 45 ducks; $45 - 6 = 39$	(1)

See pages 46–47.

37	**0**	In order: 0, 0, 0, 17, 43; the median is the middle value	(1)

See pages 146–147.

38	**hexagonal pyramid**	Seven faces (one hexagonal base, six isosceles triangles); tetrahedron has four faces; pentagonal pyramid has six faces; cube has six faces	(1)

See pages 100–101.

39	**25.5 m²**	Subtract from 6×5 rectangle probably easiest; $30 - 4.5 = 25.5$	(1)

See pages 94–95.

40	**6**	$2x - 8 = 4$ (subtract x from each side); $2x = 12$ (add 8 to each side); $x = 6$ (divide each side by 2)	(1)

See pages 128–129.

41	$\frac{14}{23}$	14 like haggis $(6+8)$; total pupils 23 $(6+8+4+5)$	(1)

See pages 134–135.

42	**£16.80**	Sale price is 60% of original; 10% is £2.80; 60% is $6 \times$ £2.80	(1)

See pages 64–65.

43	**106**	The next after 106 is 115, then 124, and so on	(1)

See pages 12–13.

44	$1\frac{1}{2}$	One-third of 6 is 2; one-sixth of 3 is one-half; $2 - \frac{1}{2} = 1\frac{1}{2}$	(1)

See pages 58–59.

45	$a - 124 - 6b$	Ahmed's height will be $a + b + 6$; Barbara's height will be $130 + 6b$; subtract $130 + 6b$ from $a + 6$	(1)

See pages 126–127.

46	**135°**	The other three angles are 135°, 45°, 45°	(1)

See pages 108–109.

47	**90**	$6 + 12 + 18 + 24 + 30$	(1)

See pages 18–19.

48	**42**	The number of grey triangles increases by 12 each time	(1)

See pages 124–125.

49	$3b = 2a$	The others all rearrange to give $a = \frac{2}{3}b$	(1)

See pages 126–127.

50	**60°**	Angles at the point where the shapes meet add to 300° (90°+60°+60°+90°); 360° − 300° = 60°	(1)

See pages 108–109.